A **D**

Dave Bush

Series editors
Ted Lister and Janet Renshaw

Stanley Thornes (Publishers) Ltd

Contents

Acknowledgements

The authors and editors would like to thank Bob Drumgoole, their colleague at Trinity School, for reading and making helpful comments on early drafts of this book. They would also like to thank pupils at Trinity School for trialling some of the material.

The authors and publisher would like to acknowledge the contribution of Steve Carpenter and Mary Edwards to the first edition.

The authors would like to thank the following for permission to reproduce photographs. Airfotos: Fig. 6.10(a); J Champion/Royal Society: Fig 1.4; N Feather/ Science Photo Library: Fig 1.3; Gianni Tortoli/Camera Press London: Fig 1.13; Llowarch's *Ripple Tank Studies in Wave Motion*, Oxford University Press: Figs 6.9(a), 6.9(b), 6.10(b), 6.10(c), 6.13; Richards, Sears, Wehr and Zermansky, *Modern College Physics*, Addison-Wesley: Fig 6.11(b); Claire Starkey: Fig. 1.5.

First published in 1992 in Great Britain by
Simon and Schuster Education

Second edition published in 1996 by Stanley Thornes (Publishers) Ltd
Ellenborough House
Wellington Street
Cheltenham
Gloucestershire GL50 1YW

        97 98 99 00 / 10 9 8 7 6 5 4 3 2

A catalogue record for this book is available from the British Library

ISBN 0-7487-2335-8

Typeset by Techset Composition Ltd
Printed and bound at Redwood Books, Trowbridge, Wiltshire

Introduction

This book is designed to help you to get ready for a post-16 course in physics: Advanced Level, Advanced Supplementary Level, BTEC, Scottish Higher, etc. The precise course you will be following doesn't matter because this book stresses the principles of physics which are the same for any course. You could use it before you begin your advanced course or during the first part of that course.* You will also find it useful if you are aiming for the higher level GCSE papers. You can also refer to it during your advanced course – especially the chapter on mathematics background. *Access to Advanced Level: Physics* has been designed so that you can work through it on your own, and the answers to all the exercises are at the end of the book. However, cheating won't help your understanding!

How to use this book

Teaching yourself how to do something needs confidence, and often that is the one thing that you don't have. We suggest that you work through each section slowly and don't move on to the next section until you have correctly answered the exercises. If you are getting most of them right you are doing well. What if you aren't? One resource is a standard physics textbook. One of the skills you will have to develop for advanced study is independent learning. There are a variety of approaches to explaining concepts and ours may not always be the best for you. At advanced level (and beyond), referring to textbooks and reading on your own initiative is going to give you a valuable skill and that essential ingredient, **confidence**, in your ability to learn by yourself.

Good luck and enjoy your physics!

Dave Bush
Bob Drumgoode

* There is a glossary of important terms at the back of the book for you to refer to.

Chapter 1

Atomic and nuclear physics

STARTING POINTS

- Do you understand the following terms; **atom, proton, neutron, electron, nucleus, energy**? Write a sentence or two (no more) to explain what you understand by each term. Then check your ideas in the glossary.

The structure of the atom

Scientists believe that atoms are made up of three main sub-atomic particles, the proton, the neutron and the electron. Their properties are summarised in Table 1.1.

Table 1.1   Sub-atomic particles

	proton	neutron	electron
approximate mass in u*	1	1	1/1840 (approximately 0)
electric charge	+1	0	− 1

* 1 atomic mass unit, u, is approximately 1.6×10^{-27} kg

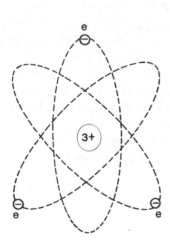

1.1   Model of a lithium atom – not to scale.

To get a better idea of the scale of the atom, think of the nucleus as being the size of a football; the electrons would be about two miles away.

Rutherford's model of the atom

In 1911 Ernest Rutherford suggested that all the mass and positive charge of the atom were contained in a very dense **nucleus** with the electrons orbiting this at some distance. He estimated that the nucleus was about 10^{-14} m across with the atom itself being about 10^{-10} m across. This meant that the diameter of the atom was 10 000 times greater than the nuclear diameter and so the atom itself was largely empty space (see Fig 1.1).

Rutherford's conclusions were based on a very clever experiment. Positively charged alpha particles were directed at a very thin (about 1/1000 mm) gold foil. Most of the alpha particles passed through the foil, confirming the idea about empty space. Many of the particles that passed through were deflected by some amount – the larger the angle of deflection the smaller the number of alpha particles deflected by that angle. A very small proportion were deflected back (see Fig 1.2).

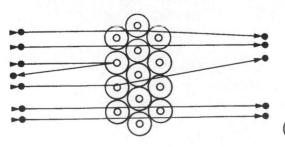

● Alpha particle

Gold atom
Gold nucleus

1.2   Scattering of alpha particles form gold foil.

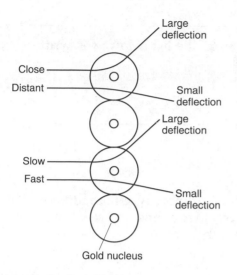

1.3 Rutherford discovered the nucleus by studying deflection of alpha particles.

Since the foil was so thin, it was likely that each deflection was caused by an interaction with a single gold nucleus. The shapes of the paths taken by the alpha particles were determined by the force which the nucleus exerted on them. By analysing the shapes of these paths, Rutherford was able to prove that the nucleus must contain a concentration of positive charge. He did not know how closely any alpha by-passed a nucleus nor which nucleus was causing the deflection, but, by studying how the deflection varied with the velocity of the alphas and how many alphas were deflected at a given angle, Rutherford showed that the force behaved like the force between positive charges (see Fig 1.3).

Neutrons and protons

Further experiments, which involved bombarding the nucleus with fast-moving particles, suggested that the nucleus contained two types of particle. These were the positively charged proton and the neutral particle or neutron. The masses of the proton and the neutron are approximately the same.

Mass number and atomic number

The mass number of an atom, sometimes given the symbol A, is the total number of nucleons (neutrons and protons) that it contains. The atomic number, sometimes given the symbol Z, is the number of protons. This is often shown in this way.

Mass no. $\qquad$ 23
$\qquad$ Symbol for element   e.g. Na for the atom sodium
Atomic no. $\qquad$ 11

So sodium has 11 protons and $(23 - 11) = 12$ neutrons.

Symbols for the elements can be found in the Periodic Table (see p. 108).

Exercise

1 Look at the following list of elements and answer the questions below.

$$^{27}_{13}Al \quad ^{75}_{33}As \quad ^{9}_{4}Be \quad ^{133}_{55}Cs$$

a How many protons are in each nucleus?
b Work out how many neutrons are in each nucleus.
c Bearing in mind that the whole atom is neutral, write down the number of electrons present in each atom.

Isotopes

Different atoms of the same element can have the same atomic number but a different mass number. This must mean that they each have the same number of protons but a different number of neutrons. These atoms are called **isotopes**. They behave chemically in the same way but have different masses. Chemical behaviour depends on the number of electrons which, in a neutral atom, is the same as the number of protons.

Exercise

2 Identify two pairs of isotopes from the list below. X is written instead of each atom's symbol.

$$^{12}_{6}X \quad ^{16}_{8}X \quad ^{17}_{8}X \quad ^{14}_{6}X$$

Table 1.2   Ionisation energies of some elements

Atom	Ionisation energy /eV
lithium	4.6
beryllium	9.4
magnesium	7.5
argon	15.7
xenon	12.1

Nuclear radiation

The nuclei of some atoms give off one or more types of radiation. This radiation can knock electrons out of other atoms (ionise them). This ionisation enables us to detect the radiation.

Ionisation

When an atom is ionised one of its outer electrons is removed. This leaves a positively charged particle called a positive **ion**. Energy is required to pull the negative electron away from the positive nucleus. This is called the **ionisation energy** of the atom. The values of the ionisation energy for some atoms are given in electronvolts in Table 1.2.

Exercise

3 Suggest what factors might affect the ease with which an electron can be removed from an atom.

The electronvolt

The electronvolt is a convenient unit for measuring very small amounts of energy. To understand it you need to remember that one volt means one joule per coulomb (see Chapter 4). So if you have a 1 V power supply, one coulomb receives one joule of energy. In a 12 V power supply:

1 C receives 1×12 J $= 12$ J of energy

0.5 C receives 0.5×12 J $= 6$ J of energy

0.1 C receives 0.1×12 J $= 1.2$ J of energy

In other words you multiply the charge, Q, by the potential difference, V, to find how much energy the charge receives from the supply.

Fig 1.4 shows an electron being accelerated between two plates. The energy the electron receives is calculated in the same way as above – multiply the charge by the potential difference.

energy given to the electron = electron charge × voltage

$$E = Q \times V$$

$$E = 1.6 \times 10^{-19} \text{ C} \times 1 \text{ V}$$

$$E = 1.6 \times 10^{-19} \text{ J}$$

This tiny amount of energy is called an electronvolt (eV).

$$1 \text{ eV} = 1.6 \times 10^{-19} \text{ J}$$

$$100 \text{ eV} = 100 \times 1.6 \times 10^{-19} = 1.6 \times 10^{-17} \text{ J}$$

So to convert electronvolts to joules just multiply by 1.6×10^{-19}.

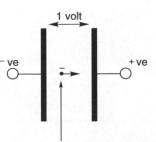

An electron (charge 1.6×10^{-19} C)

1.4   An electron being accelerated by a potential difference.

Example

1.5 Photograph of alpha particle tracks in a cloud chamber.

What is the speed of a 1 eV electron?

The energy given to the electron is present as kinetic energy (KE).

$KE = \frac{1}{2}mv^2$, (see Chapter 2) where m is the mass and v the speed, and a 1 eV electron has 1.6×10^{-19} J of KE, so we can write:

$$\frac{1}{2}mv^2 = 1.6 \times 10^{-19} \text{ J}$$

Multiplying both sides by 2

$$mv^2 = 3.2 \times 10^{-19} \text{ J}$$

Dividing both sides by m

$$v^2 = \frac{3.2 \times 10^{-19} \text{ J}}{m}$$

The mass of an electron $= 9.1 \times 10^{-31}$ kg, so

$$v^2 = \frac{3.2 \times 10^{-19} \text{ J}}{9.1 \times 10^{-31} \text{ kg}}$$

$$v^2 = 3.5 \times 10^{11} \text{ m}^2/\text{s}^2$$

$$v = 5.9 \times 10^5 \text{ m/s}$$

This electron is no slouch. The electron has such a small mass that even a mere 1 eV of energy gives it a high speed.

Exercise

4 What would be the speed of a 4 eV electron? (Take care; work it out because the answer is not 4 times the velocity of a 1 eV electron.)

The cloud chamber

A cloud chamber shows up the path of ionising radiation. The air inside the chamber is saturated with vapour. When the radiation passes through, it leaves ions in its wake. The vapour condenses on these ions, forming tiny droplets. These droplets indicate the path taken by the ions. This is rather like the vapour trail of an aircraft.

The radiation itself uses up energy every time it ionises an atom. There is, therefore, a maximum length of track depending on the energy of the particular radiation.

Nuclei give out different types of radiation which can be recognised from the kinds of track they produce. They are named after letters of the Greek alphabet. Have a look at Figs 1.5 and 1.6.

The tracks in Fig 1.5 are thick and straight. They are caused by **alpha radiation**.

The thin tracks in Fig 1.6 are caused by **beta radiation**.

1.6 Photograph of beta particle tracks in a cloud chamber.

Exercise

5 Alpha radiation produces more ions per centimetre travelled than does beta radiation. It also travels more slowly. Use this information to explain the differences in the tracks they make in the cloud chamber.

6 The beta tracks are thinner. What does this tell you about the number of ions produced per millimetre of track?

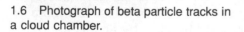

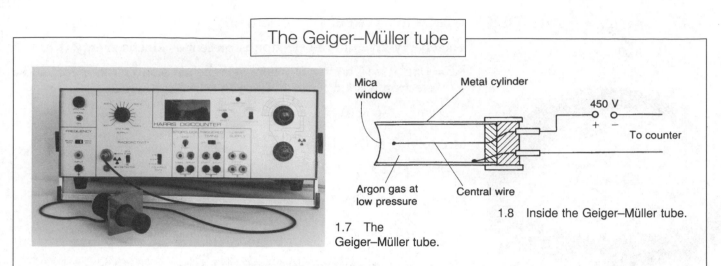

The Geiger–Müller tube

1.7 The Geiger–Müller tube.

1.8 Inside the Geiger–Müller tube.

This instrument is used to 'count' radioactive particles. The particles enter through the thin window and cause ionisation of the gas atoms inside the tube. This produces Ar^+ ions and electrons. The negative electrons are attracted by the positive central wire and accelerate towards it while the positive ions move towards the inner wall of the tube. If the voltage between the central wire and the walls is large enough then these particles will ionise atoms that they collide with on the way. In this way an avalanche of moving charge is created. It is this avalanche which is registered to indicate that a particle of ionising radiation has passed into the tube.

Exercise

7 As the alpha particle progresses it loses energy. What happens to its velocity?

Types of radiation

Look back at the cloud chamber photographs, Figs 1.5 and 1.6. The different types of tracks are caused by the different properties of the radiation which passes through.

We can identify three types of nuclear radiation. These are **alpha radiation**, symbol, α; **beta radiation**, symbol, β; and **gamma radiation**, symbol, γ.

Alpha radiation

This can be stopped by a thick sheet of paper, your clothing or even your skin and will only travel a few centimetres in air as it causes intense ionisation of the gas molecules because it collides with them so often. It can be deflected from a straight line path by an electric or magnetic field. The size and direction of these deflections suggest that alpha radiation consists of particles with a particular mass and charge. The mass and charge are the same as those of a helium ion, He^{2+}. In fact Rutherford collected the gas formed when alpha particles were trapped in a tube and showed that it was helium.

So, an alpha particle is simply a particle composed of two neutrons and two protons which is thrown out of the nucleus of the original atom.

Exercise

8 Write down the mass number and the atomic number for an alpha particle.

1.9　The deflections of alpha, beta and gamma radiation in a magnetic field.

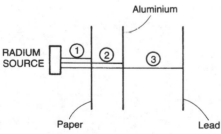

1.11　Absorption of radiation.

Beta radiation

This has a greater range than alpha radiation and can actually travel several metres in air. It will pass through paper but can be stopped by a few millimetres of aluminium. It produces fewer ions per centimetre of travel than does alpha radiation. The sizes and directions of the deflections of beta radiation in magnetic (see Fig 1.9) and electric fields show that beta radiation consists of fast-moving electrons. So the beta particle is much less massive than an alpha particle (about 1/7000) and carries a single negative charge.

Gamma radiation

This is extremely penetrating. It is not completely stopped even by several centimetres of lead. It produces fewer ions per centimetre of travel than does beta radiation of comparable energy and far fewer than does comparable alpha radiation. It is not deflected by electric or magnetic fields which suggests that it is not charged. It is possible however to show both **interference** and **diffraction** with it. This suggests that it consists of waves (see Chapter 6).

In fact, gamma radiation is very short wavelength **electromagnetic waves** and it travels at the speed of light.

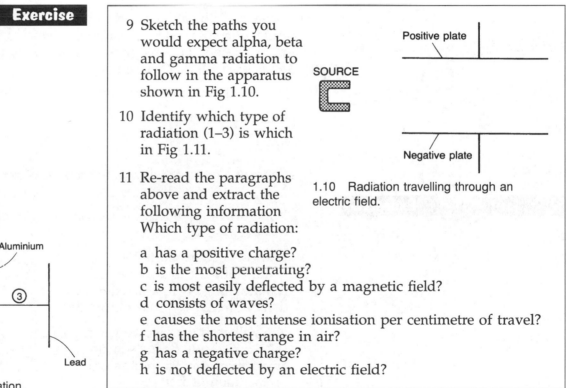

9　Sketch the paths you would expect alpha, beta and gamma radiation to follow in the apparatus shown in Fig 1.10.

10　Identify which type of radiation (1–3) is which in Fig 1.11.

11　Re-read the paragraphs above and extract the following information
Which type of radiation:

a　has a positive charge?
b　is the most penetrating?
c　is most easily deflected by a magnetic field?
d　consists of waves?
e　causes the most intense ionisation per centimetre of travel?
f　has the shortest range in air?
g　has a negative charge?
h　is not deflected by an electric field?

1.10　Radiation travelling through an electric field.

Nuclear transformations

Since all of these different types of radiation come out of the nucleus, then the composition of the nucleus must be affected when radiation is given off. We say that the nucleus has decayed.

Alpha decay

Radium, for example, gives out an alpha particle. This must mean a loss of two protons and two neutrons from the nucleus.

This can be expressed using the atomic number and the mass number in a so-called nuclear equation.

$$_{88}^{226}\mathrm{Ra} \rightarrow\ _{86}^{222}\mathrm{Rn} +\ _{2}^{4}\mathrm{He}$$

The number of protons in the nucleus has been reduced from 88 to 86, while the total number of nucleons has been reduced from 226 to 222. This means that a different element has been produced. In this case the new element has atomic number 86 which is radon, symbol Rn.

Notice that the top numbers balance on each side of the equation as do the bottom numbers. The nuclear equation only deals with the particles in the nucleus, not with the electrons.

12 Radon-222 is a gas which is radioactive. It decays to polonium, Po, by giving out an alpha particle. Write down the nuclear equation to describe this transformation.

Beta decay

Beta decay is a little more complicated. There are no electrons in the nucleus. What happens is that one of the neutrons changes into a proton plus an electron. The proton stays in the nucleus and the electron is emitted as a beta particle.

This means that the atomic number (the number of protons) actually increases by one. The total mass number remains the same, as a proton has approximately the same mass as a neutron, and the mass of an electron is so small that we can neglect it.

Thorium-234 decays to protactinium-234 by emitting a beta particle.

The nuclear equation will be

$$_{90}^{234}\mathrm{Th} \rightarrow\ _{91}^{234}\mathrm{Pa} +\ _{-1}^{0}\mathrm{e}$$

$_{-1}^{0}$e stands for a beta particle as it has a mass of zero and a charge of −1.

13 Write down the nuclear equations for the following transformations.

a lead-211 to bismuth-211
b francium-221 to astatine-217
c plutonium-241 to americium-241
d thorium-231 to protactinium-231

You will need the following symbols and atomic numbers: lead, Pb, 82; bismuth, Bi, 83; francium, Fr, 87; astatine, At, 85; americium, Am, 95; plutonium, Pu, 94; thorium, Th, 90; protactinium, Pa, 91.

Fission and fusion

The protons and neutrons in atomic nuclei are held together by the strongest known force, called the **strong nuclear force**. This means that they have locked up in them a great deal of energy. Some heavy nuclei such as those of uranium can split into parts with a release of some of this energy. This process is called **nuclear fission**. It is the source of the energy generated in nuclear reactors.

Light nuclei such as hydrogen can join together with release of energy in a process called **nuclear fusion**. This is the source of the energy produced by the sun and in the hydrogen bomb. We will look at fission and fusion in more detail in Chapter 7.

Radioactive decay

The changes that occur when a radioactive substance decays are not like chemical changes. They cannot be controlled and they are not affected by physical conditions such as temperature or pressure, neither are they affected by the element involved being chemically combined. Also, the energy released in radioactive decay is enormously greater than that in chemical changes.

The chance nature of radioactive decay

The decay of radioactive nuclei is a random process. In practice each nucleus of a particular isotope has the same chance of decay as any other but it is impossible to say which one will decay at a given time. However, if you have a very large number of nuclei, this random behaviour results in smooth, predictable patterns. Put simply, the more nuclei you have, the more will decay at a given time. If you halve the number of nuclei you will halve the number decaying. This kind of behaviour can be summarised in an equation:

Rate of decay $= k \times$ number of nuclei

This means that the rate of decay is proportional to the number of nuclei present. If you plot a graph of decay rate against time you get a smooth curve like the one in Fig 1.12. This is an **exponential** curve: in successive equal time intervals the rate of decay falls by a fixed fraction. An important time interval is the one in which the rate of decay falls by half. This is called the **half-life** of the source. A particular isotope always has the same half-life.

Half-lives can vary from fractions of a second up to millions of years.

The graph in Fig 1.12 shows how the activity of a source (the number of nuclei which decay in a given time) varies with time. You can see from the graph that every half-life, the activity decreases by a half. To find the half-life from a graph, we can start from *any* point and find how long it takes for the activity to drop to half the value.

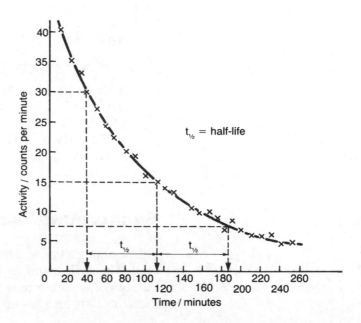

1.12 The half-life of this substance is 73 minutes.

Example

A Strontium-90 is radioactive and decays by beta emission. It has a half-life of 28 years. A 1 g sample of pure strontium-90 contains about 6.7×10^{21} atoms.

a How many atoms will be present after 28 years?

6.7×10^{21} atoms remain. A trick question! Each atom which decays emits a beta particle but is still present even though it is now an atom of yttrium.

b How many strontium-90 atoms will be present in the sample after 28 years?

3.35×10^{21}. The half-life is 28 years, so half the strontium-90 atoms will have decayed. In fact they will have become atoms of yttrium.

B Technetium-99 is a radioactive isotope which can be used in medicine to monitor bone growth. The isotope can be dissolved and the solution given to the patient. Technetium-99 has a half-life of 6 hours. A sample is prepared at 4 p.m. on Tuesday and has an activity of 4000 counts per minute. A patient is treated at 10 a.m. on the next day. What is the activity of the technetium?

> 4 p.m. to 10 a.m. is 18 hours.
> 18 hours is 3 half-lives, therefore the activity halves 3 times
> $4000/2 = 2000$
> $2000/2 = 1000$
> $1000/2 = 500$

The activity of the technetium is 500 counts per minute when the patient is treated.

Exercise

14 The results shown in Table 1.3 are from an experiment to measure the activity of a radioactive element at different times.

Table 1.3   Radioactive decay

Time/minutes	Activity/counts per second
0.0	1340
1.0	834
1.8	584
3.0	340
5.0	134

a Plot a graph of activity (vertically) against time (horizontally).
b Use this graph to find the half life of the substance.
c After three half-lives what would you expect for the value of the activity of the substance? Show how you arrive at this value.

Background radiation

The results given in Table 1.3 were taken using a Geiger–Müller tube. This will count *all* the radiation entering it, not just that from the source we are interested in. Radiation from radioactive materials in rocks and air and also cosmic rays will all be counted. This is called

background radiation. To find the actual activity of the source we must subtract this background radiation from each of the measured counts. We can measure the background radiation by taking a count without the source present. In question 14 above, the background count was 4 counts per second so the observed count at time 0 would have been 1344 counts per second.

Exercise

15 Work out the actual observed count rate for the reading taken after 3.0 minutes in question 14.

Radiocarbon dating

The carbon present in the carbon dioxide in the atmosphere contains a small proportion of the radioactive isotope carbon-14 produced by cosmic rays. Knowing the half-life of this substance means that the age of material which has once lived can be determined. All material that is living, or has once lived, contains carbon. The amount of radioactive carbon reduces with time as it decays but in a living substance the carbon is continually replaced by respiration. This means that a certain amount of living material always contains a constant and unchanging amount of radioactive carbon.

When the material dies, however, the carbon is no longer replaced and hence the amount of radioactive carbon *does* reduce with time. The activity of radioactive carbon in living material is approximately 16 counts per minute for every gram of carbon. Carbon-14 has a half-life of approximately 5600 years.

1.13   The Turin shroud has been dated by the radiocarbon method.

Example

A piece of wood is found whose carbon-14 activity was found to be two counts per minute per gram of wood. What is its age?

When the wood died, the carbon-14 activity would have been 16 counts per minute per gram. This will reduce by half every 5600 years. So after 5600 years the activity would have been 8 counts per minute per gram; 5600 years later still, 4 counts per minute per gram; and a further 5600 years later, 2 counts per minute per gram. So the age of the object must be 5600 + 5600 + 5600 = 16 800 years.

Exercise

16 A piece of wood found in an archaeological excavation can be tested to find its approximate age. Use the following steps to find its age.

a What would you expect the activity of 5 grams of carbon in the living wood to be?
b When 5 grams of the carbon from the excavated wood was tested the activity was found to be 20 counts per minute. Can you suggest an approximate age for the wood?

Chapter 2 ▸ Energy

STARTING POINTS

● Do you understand the following terms: **energy**, **work**, **force**? Write a sentence or two (no more) to explain what you understand by each term, then check in the glossary.

Work and energy

Work and energy are two words we often use in everyday conversation. In physics we use these words in a precise way and with agreed definitions.

Early ideas on work were influenced by the fact that tasks were usually accomplished by people or animals pushing this or pulling that. The outcome was determined by just how big a force could be applied and work was defined in relation to this force.

The physicist's definition is that work is done when a force moves. Anything with the capacity to do work has energy. In physics, work only means moving the point of action of a force. So thinking about your homework is not doing work in the physics sense, but playing tennis is. A shelf holding up some books is providing a force, but as it is not moving, the shelf is doing no work.

Exercise

1 In which of the following situations is work being done?

   a An executive making decisions.
   b A pillar holding up a bridge.
   c A weightlifter making a lift.
   d A hockey player scoring a goal.
   e Your chair, holding you off the floor.

Do not forget that when work is done, energy is being transferred to something else. This means that when you measure the work, you have also measured the energy transferred.

Measuring work

The larger the force you use, the more work you do.

The further you push, the more work you do.

The amount of work, W, depends on:

   the size of the force, F, (measured in newtons)
   the distance it moves, d, (measured in metres)

In fact

   work = force × distance (in the direction of the force)

   $W = F \times d$

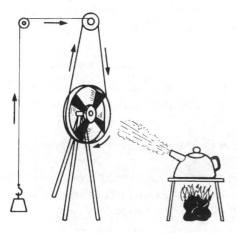

2.1 A lump of coal can do work.

If you double the force, you will double the work or if you double the distance you will double the work. This is what you feel intuitively, so we say that the equation behaves in a sensible way, i.e. it does what you expect.

In this equation you multiply newtons by metres so the unit of work is the newton metre which is called a joule. The joule is defined as the work done when a force of 1 N moves through a distance of 1 m. It takes a force of about 1 newton to lift an average-sized apple. So if you lift an apple from a kitchen floor onto a 1 m high worktop, you have done 1 joule of work and transferred 1 joule of your energy to the apple. As energy is transformed, work is being done. Work and energy have the same units. Energy can be compared to having money in your pocket, whilst work can be compared to spending it.

Example

A How much work is done in pushing a car 1500 m with a force of 400 N?

$$W = F \times d$$
$$w = 400 \text{ N} \times 1500 \text{ m}$$
$$w = 600\,000 \text{ J}$$

How much energy has been transferred?

Energy transferred $= 600\,000$ J

B A man uses 1000 J of energy lifting a sack of apples 2 m. What force does he use?

$$W = F \times d$$

So, rearranging the equation

$$F = \frac{W}{d}$$
$$F = \frac{1000 \text{ J}}{2 \text{ m}}$$
$$= 500 \text{ N}$$

Exercise

2 A cyclist pushes her bicycle with a force of 200 N for a distance of 6320 m. How much work does she do?

3 A car uses 8000 J of energy in moving 20 m. How much force does the engine push the car with?

4 A motorcycle has 60 000 J of movement energy. If the brakes deliver a stopping force of 500 N what is the shortest distance the motorcyclist can stop in?

Conservation of energy

The principle of conservation of energy is of fundamental importance. It states that energy can neither be destroyed nor created. It is based on the results of numerous very rigorous experiments. Physicists have absolute faith in this principle and use it when analysing other results. It was instrumental in the discovery of the neutrino – a massless, chargeless 'ghost' particle.

Conservation means that our example of pushing the car is not as simple as it seems. Work has been done, energy has been transferred but at the end of the exercise the car is at rest. What has happened to the energy? Where do you think it has gone?

Types of energy

To answer these questions we need to remember that energy exists in a range of forms and in many processes it changes from one form into others.

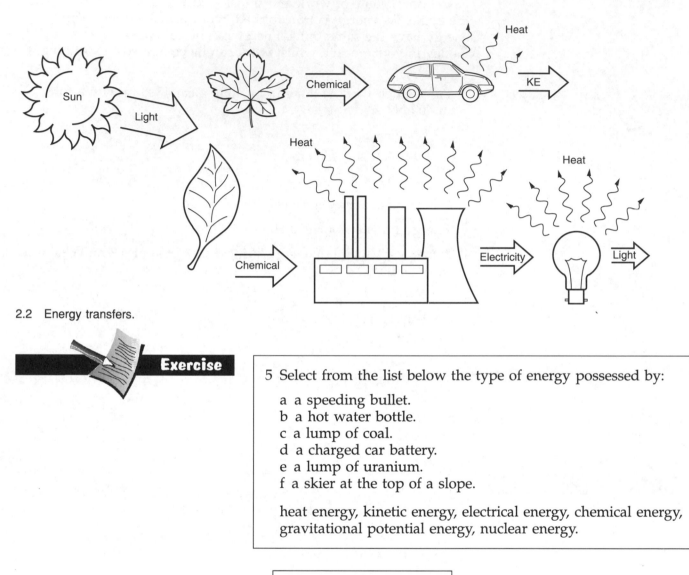

2.2   Energy transfers.

Exercise

5 Select from the list below the type of energy possessed by:

a a speeding bullet.
b a hot water bottle.
c a lump of coal.
d a charged car battery.
e a lump of uranium.
f a skier at the top of a slope.

heat energy, kinetic energy, electrical energy, chemical energy, gravitational potential energy, nuclear energy.

Joule and Rumford

Scientists once called heat 'caloric' and imagined it to be some kind of fluid. They were convinced that it was conserved and explained friction burns in terms of caloric being squeezed out of things.

A Bavarian cannon maker called Count Rumford noticed that using blunt drills led to an almost limitless supply of caloric. He suggested that caloric might be energy after all. He was not taken seriously.

This idea was developed by James Joule in a very long series of experiments. He churned water, he churned mercury, he rubbed iron plates together, he even measured water temperatures at the top and bottom of a waterfall whilst on honeymoon. As a result of all this effort he helped to establish that heat and energy really were the same thing. The unit of energy was named after him.

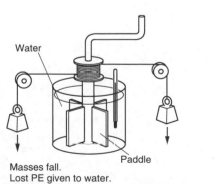

Masses fall.
Lost PE given to water.
Paddle disconnected to allow mass to be raised again.
Led to a value for amount of energy needed to raise 1 g by 1°C

2.3   Joule's water-churning experiment.

Energy calculations

Different types of energy are calculated using different equations. You need to remember the equations and also the fact that energy is conserved. The general strategy for dealing with energy calculations is:

In simple situations

1 Identify the type of energy involved and write the relevant equation.
2 Insert values in the equation and solve.

In more complicated situations energy will change from one form to another

3 Identify the energy changes involved.
4 Set 'lost' energy = 'gained' energy.
5 Insert values in the equations.
6 Find the unknown quantity.

Now we can look at how to calculate each type of energy.

Potential energy

The word 'potential' simply means stored, and under the right conditions the energy can be released. Fuels, food and springs all have potential energy.

Gravitational potential energy

This is the type of energy an object has when it is raised above the ground. We can see how to measure the amount of gravitational potential energy that an object has by thinking about how much work we had to do to get it there. For example, imagine carrying a rucksack to the top of a flight of stairs. Your work to get it (and you) to the top would differ with the mass of the sack and the height of the flight of stairs. The other important factor is the gravitational pull of the Earth.

Gravitational Potential Energy (GPE) = mgh

m = mass in kg
g = gravitational field strength (10 N/kg on the Earth's surface)
h = height in m above some reference point – often the Earth's surface

Example

A A weightlifter raises 250 kg through 2 m. If the gravitational field strength is 10 N/kg, what is the energy gained by the mass?

$$GPE = mgh \qquad \text{(Identify energy form and write equation)}$$
$$= 250 \text{ kg} \times 10 \text{ N/kg} \times 2 \text{ m} \qquad \text{(Insert values)}$$
$$= 5000 \text{ J} \qquad \text{(Simplify)}$$

The weightlifter is on a competition platform 1.5 m high. What is the gravitational potential energy relative to the ground?

total height = 2 + 1.5 = 3.5 m

$$GPE = mgh$$
$$= 250 \text{ kg} \times 10 \text{ N/kg} \times 3.5 \text{ m}$$
$$= 8750 \text{ J}$$

B On a building site a bricklayer drops a brick and it falls 5 m to the ground. The brick reaches the ground with 100 J of energy.

What was the mass of the brick?

$$GPE = mgh \qquad \text{(Identify energy form and write equation)}$$
$$100\,\text{J} = m \times 10\,\text{N/kg} \times 5\,\text{m} \qquad \text{(Insert values)}$$
$$100 = m \times 50 \qquad \text{(Simplify)}$$
$$\frac{100}{50} = m$$
$$m = 2\,\text{kg}$$

Where does $E = mgh$ come from?

The equation for gravitational potential energy is nothing more than a modification of our basic equation:

  work done = force × distance

When you lift something the force you need is equal to the weight of the object:

  force = weight = mg

The distance is the height lifted, h.

So we use these in the equation and work done becomes mgh.

Exercise

2.4 Testing a Roman catapult.

(Take $g = 10$ N/kg throughout.)

6 How much energy is needed to carry a toddler of mass 11 kg from road level to the 12th floor of a building 36 m above.

7 A catapult has 20 J of energy to project a marble of mass 0.005 kg upwards. What is the maximum height the marble can reach above the catapult.

8 The water from a hydroelectric power station can release 40×10^6 J of energy falling through 40 m. What mass of water must be used in this process?

9 A golf ball can be thrown 40 m up into the air on Earth. How much higher could it be thrown on the moon where the gravity is only 1.6 N/kg? Hint: assume the ball gains the same amount of PE in each case.

10 A Roman catapult (Fig 2.4) relied on a heavy mass falling to the ground to launch a smaller mass into the air. If a mass of 200 kg is allowed to fall 3 m:

   a how much PE did the mass have before it fell?
   b what is the maximum energy the mass can have?
   c if the smaller mass rose 10 m what is its mass?

Kinetic energy

Moving objects have energy. This energy is called kinetic energy and can be calculated using the equation:

  $KE = \frac{1}{2}mv^2$

where m is the mass and v the velocity.

From the equation you can see that KE depends on both the mass and the velocity. Velocity is more important because it is squared.

$$v = 5 \xrightarrow{\text{(double velocity)}} v = 10 \xrightarrow{\text{(double velocity)}} v = 20$$
$$v^2 = 25 \qquad\qquad v^2 = 100 \qquad\qquad v^2 = 400$$

so if you double the velocity, you quadruple the velocity squared.

Try to remember that squared values are more significant.

Example

A A car of mass 750 kg is moving at a velocity of 10 m/s. What is its kinetic energy?

$$KE = \tfrac{1}{2}mv^2$$
$$= \tfrac{1}{2} \times 750 \text{ kg} \times 10 \text{ m/s} \times 10 \text{ m/s}$$
$$= 37\,500 \text{ J}$$

B A 2 kg brick hit the ground with 100 J of energy. How fast was it travelling as it hit the ground?

$$KE = \tfrac{1}{2}mv^2 \qquad\qquad \text{(Identify energy form and write equation)}$$
$$100 = \tfrac{1}{2} \times 2 \times v^2 \qquad\qquad \text{(Insert values)}$$
$$100 = v^2 \qquad\qquad \text{(Simplify)}$$
$$10 = v \qquad\qquad \text{(Take square roots)}$$
$$v = 10 \text{ m/s}$$

Exercise

11 What is the KE of a runner with a mass of 80 kg travelling at 10 m/s.

12 If a 40 000 kg truck is travelling at 30 m/s what is its KE?

13 A rounders' ball is thrown with a velocity of 25 m/s. What is its KE if its mass is 0.3 kg?

14 If a skateboarder of mass 50 kg has a KE of 1600 J, how fast is she going?

15 A motorbike when travelling at 20 m/s has a KE of 50 000 J. What is the mass of the bike?

Energy exchanges

The calculations we have looked at so far only involve considering one form of energy. In energy transfers, where energy is transformed from one form to another, you need to be able to identify the appropriate energy forms.

For example, an object falls from a shelf. It started with gravitational potential energy (because of its height). Once any body starts to fall it accelerates. As it does so, its potential energy is turned increasingly into kinetic energy. When the object is about to hit the floor all the potential energy has turned into kinetic energy. This means we can say

Where does $E = \frac{1}{2}mv^2$ come from?

To start something moving you have to apply a force and the force moves with the object. We can use this to derive the kinetic energy equation.

Imagine you are throwing a rock with a steady force.

$\qquad$ work done on the rock $= F \times d$

where F is the force and d the distance

This is the energy you give to the rock. So,

$\qquad$ KE $= F \times d$

But we know that

$\qquad$ $F = m \times a$

where a is the acceleration. So now,

$\qquad$ KE $= m \times a \times d$

From our equations of uniformly accelerated motion (see p. 37) we know that $s = ut + \frac{1}{2}at^2$. If the rock starts from rest then $u = 0$ and $s = \frac{1}{2}at^2$.

We can use this for the distance d and the equation for kinetic energy becomes

$$KE = m \times a \times \tfrac{1}{2}at^2$$
$$\quad = m \times \tfrac{1}{2}(at)^2$$

But the velocity is equal to acceleration times the time, so $at = v$ and we can now write KE as

$$KE = \tfrac{1}{2}mv^2$$

$$KE = PE$$
$$\tfrac{1}{2}mv^2 = mgh$$
$$mv^2 = 2mgh$$
$$v^2 = 2gh$$

and so we can calculate the impact velocity.

Example

A rock is dropped from a height of 4 m. What will its velocity be when it hits the ground?

Interpreting equations
$v^2 = 2gh$ is another equation with a squared value so you need to be cautious when using it to make predictions. You might predict that if you double the height, the rock would hit the ground at twice the speed. It doesn't – put in the values and see.

$KE = PE$	(Identify the energy change and write equations)
$\tfrac{1}{2}mv^2 = mgh$	(Energy gain = Energy lost)
$mv^2 = 2mgh$	(Simplify – multiply each side by 2)
$v^2 = 2gh$	(Simplify – divide both sides by m)
$v^2 = 2 \times 10 \text{ N/kg} \times 4 \text{ m}$	
$v^2 = 80$	(Take the square root)
$v = 8.9 \text{ m/s}$	

Note that in this problem you do not need to know the mass. If a variable appears on both sides of an equation then it cancels out. This is useful to remember.

When a car brakes what happens to its kinetic energy? Owing to the friction in the brakes the kinetic energy is converted into heat. The car uses up its energy in working against the frictional force. So a force is applied to the car and this force moves through the braking distance (see Fig 2.5).

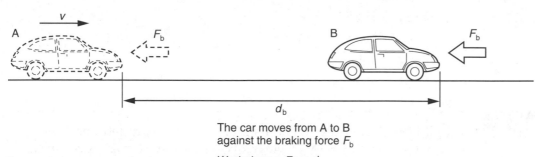

The car moves from A to B
against the braking force F_b

Work done = $F_b \times d_b$

2.5   The work done in stopping a car.

work done by braking force = braking force × braking distance

$$= F_b \times d_b$$

Since this equals the kinetic energy:

$$F_b \times d_b = \tfrac{1}{2}mv^2$$

 **Example**

A car of mass 1000 kg is travelling at 12 m/s. After the brakes are applied it travels for 15 m before it comes to rest. What is the average braking force produced by the brakes?

work done by braking force = KE

                          (Identify energy change and write equations)

$F_b \times d_b = \tfrac{1}{2}mv^2$ (Energy loss = Energy gain)

$F_b \times 15\ \text{m} = \tfrac{1}{2} \times 1000\ \text{kg} \times 12^2\ \text{m}^2/\text{s}^2$ (Insert values)

$15\,F_b = 72\,000\ \text{J}$ (Simplify)

$F_b = \dfrac{72\,000}{15}$ (Divide both sides by 15)

$F_b = 4800\ \text{N}$

 **Exercise**

16 A cat knocks a flower pot from a window sill. If the distance to the ground is 3.0 m what will be the impact velocity?

17 A car has a mass of 1000 kg and is carrying passengers with a mass 200 kg. The driver applies the brakes when it is travelling at 12 m/s. If the braking force is 4800 N what distance will it travel before coming to rest?

Spring energy

If you want to stretch a spring then you have to apply a force and move the force. This is another example of doing work. The amount of work done is equal to the energy stored in the spring.

energy stored in the spring $=\frac{1}{2}Fx$

$F=$ maximum force applied

$x=$ extension of spring

In an experiment a steel spring was stretched by 24 cm (0.24 m). The force needed to do this was 8 N. How much energy was stored in the spring?

Example

$$\text{energy} = \frac{1}{2}Fx$$
$$= \frac{1}{2} \times 8\,\text{N} \times 0.24\,\text{m}$$
$$= 0.96\,\text{J}$$

Exercise

18 In the same experiment a stiffer spring was tested and 8 N stretched it by only 20 cm. How much energy was stored in this spring?

19 Two of these stiffer springs were then mounted side by side and 8 N was again applied.

    a What force would be stretching each spring?
    b What would each spring extend by?
    c What total energy would be stored?

Springs behave elastically within limits. This means that if the force stretching a spring is increased in equal steps then the extension increases in equal steps. So if 10 N causes an extension of 2 cm in a spring, then 20 N will cause an extension of 4 cm, and so on.

A spring gave the following results in an experiment (Table 2.1):

Table 2.1   Experimental results

Force in N	Extension in cm	Force/Extension in N/cm
10	2	10/2 = 5
20	4	20/4 = 5
30	6	30/6 = 5
40	8	40/8 = 5
50	10	50/10 = 5

When we divide the force by the extension we get the same number. This number is called the **spring constant**, k, (sometimes called the **stiffness**) and indicates the force needed per unit of extension. We can use it to determine the force needed for any extension.

For example, what force is needed to produce an extension of 2.5 cm?

1 cm extension needs 5 N
2.5 cm extension needs 5 N/cm × 2.5 cm = 12.5 N

This gives us another equation

force = spring constant × extension
$$F = kx$$

We can now use this in the energy equation

$$\text{energy} = \tfrac{1}{2}Fx \qquad (\text{Put } F = kx)$$
$$= \tfrac{1}{2}(kx)x$$
$$= \tfrac{1}{2}kx^2$$

Where does $E = \tfrac{1}{2}Fx$ come from?

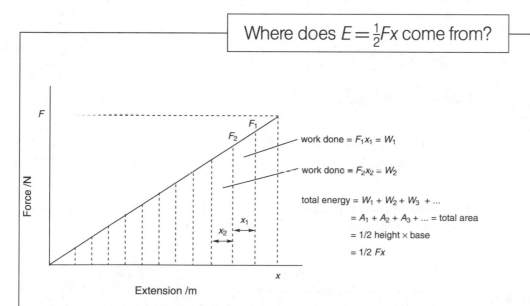

2.6   Force–extension graph for a spring.

The graph in Fig 2.6 shows that the extension is proportional to force. The graph is divided up into strips. Each strip represents a small change in extension. Now concentrate on the shaded strip. For this strip the force increases from F_1 to F_2 and the spring increases in length by x_1.

   work done in stretching by x_1 = (approx) F_1x_1 (from work done = force × distance)

If we make x_1 even smaller this becomes a better approximation.

To find the total energy we could do this for all the strips and add the energy elements together.

If, however, you think of the shaded strip as an approximate rectangle then

   area of strip $= F_1x_1$

and so the area and the energy element are equal. Adding all the energy elements together is the same as adding all the areas. This means that the area under the graph is the total energy.

Since the graph is a triangle,

   Area $= \tfrac{1}{2}$ height × base
        $= \tfrac{1}{2}$ maximum force × extension

Therefore

   Energy stored $= \tfrac{1}{2}Fx$

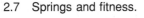

Example

A fitness machine, used for toning muscles, is fitted with four steel springs each of stiffness 200 N/m. The number of springs can be varied depending on the user's strength.

A What would be the stiffness of the 4 springs in parallel?

Answer   800 N/m

In parallel the springs share the force so for a given extension you need 4 times the force for one spring.

B How much energy is needed to stretch one spring 40 cm?

$$\text{energy} = \tfrac{1}{2}kx^2 \qquad \text{(Identify energy change and write equation)}$$
$$= \tfrac{1}{2} \times 200 \text{ N/m} \times 0.4^2 \text{ m}^2 \text{ (Insert values} - \text{extension in m)}$$
$$= 16 \text{ J}$$

C How much energy would be needed to stretch the spring twice as much?

$$\text{energy} = \tfrac{1}{2}kx^2$$

Extension is 0.8 m.

$$\text{energy} = \tfrac{1}{2} \times 200 \text{ N/m} \times 0.8^2 \text{ m}^2$$
$$= 64 \text{ J}$$

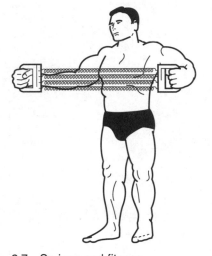

2.7   Springs and fitness.

Note that doubling the extension increases the energy 4 times. This is another example of a squared value in an equation.

Exercise

20 Jennifer is designing a toy as part of her design project. It is made from a compression spring and will have a plastic frog on top. When pressed down a rubber sucker should hold it firmly for a time. The fun bit for a child is that it springs up unexpectedly.

  a When the toy is compressed what type of energy is stored in it?
  b When released what happens to this energy?
    The spring compresses by 3 cm and has a spring constant of 100 N/m.
  c How much energy can be stored in the spring?
  d Jennifer wants the frog to jump up 10 cm. What is the maximum mass it can have? (Hint: PE = spring energy.)

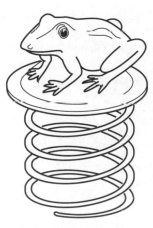

2.8   Springs and toys.

Internal energy

When we heat a body it absorbs energy. This energy can cause the temperature to rise or the material to change state. The energy under these circumstances is absorbed by the molecules of the material and increases the **internal energy** of the material.

Heat energy

Did you know that water has a very high specific heat capacity? This makes it an excellent liquid for hot water bottles.

The amount of energy stored in a hot object depends on its temperature, its mass and also the material it is made of – some materials store more heat than others. The ability of a material to store heat is measured by the **specific heat capacity**, c. It tells us how much heat energy has been stored in 1 kg of the material when it has been heated by 1 °C. It is measured in J/kg/°C.

We can only use the energy stored in a hot body by transferring it to a colder body, so in heat energy problems we deal with heat *change*.

For example when heating water, 4200 J will raise the temperature of 1 kg by 1 °C. The specific heat capacity of water is therefore 4200 J/kg/°C. We can use this pattern to produce an equation.

To heat 1 kg of water through 1 °C requires 4200 J
To heat 2 kg of water through 1 °C requires 2 × 4200 J
To heat 3 kg of water through 1 °C requires 3 × 4200 J
To heat 3 kg of water through 2 °C requires 3 × 4200 × 2 J

So in general

heat change = mass × specific heat capacity × temperature change

heat change $= mcT$

where

$m =$ mass in kg

$c =$ specific heat capacity in J/kg/°C

$T =$ temperature change in °C

We can use this equation with any material provided we know the value of the specific heat capacity of the material.

 **Example**

A A saucepan of water is heated from 20 °C to 100 °C. The specific heat capacity of water is 4200 J/kg/°C. The mass of the water is 2 kg, how much heat energy is stored in the water?

heat energy $= mcT$
$= 2 \text{ kg} × 4200 \text{ J/kg/°C} × 80 \text{ °C}$
$= 672\,000 \text{ J}$

B In a physics lesson, Kuldip was given a 200 g block of aluminium and was asked to find its specific heat capacity. He put the block in boiling water and after 5 minutes transferred it into 150 g of water at 20 °C. The final temperature of the aluminium and water was 37 °C. What value does this give for the specific heat capacity of aluminium?

In this problem the heat lost by the aluminium is gained by the water.

heat lost by aluminium = heat gained by water
$$m_a c_a T_a = m_w c_w T_w$$

Remember to convert all masses to kg.

Insert the value of masses in kg and insert the temperature *changes*. Note that the temperature of the aluminium has dropped from 100 °C to 37 °C and that of the water has risen from 20 °C to 37 °C.

$$0.2 \times c_a \times (100 - 37) = 0.15 \times 4200 \times (37 - 20)$$
$$0.2 \times c_a \times 63 = 0.15 \times 4200 \times 17$$
$$12.6 \times c_a = 10\,710$$
$$c_a = \frac{10\,710}{12.6}$$
$$c_a = 850 \text{ J/kg/}^\circ\text{C}$$

Exercise

21   How much energy is required to heat a room of air whose mass is 24 kg, by 15 °C? The specific heat capacity of air is 100 J/kg/ °C.

22   A storage heater requires 4.2×10^6 J to heat it by 20 °C. If its mass is 100 kg what is the specific heat capacity of the storage material?

23   A brick of mass 2 kg is heated from 60 °C to 70 °C. If the specific heat capacity of the brick is 3000 J/kg/°C how much energy is used to heat it?

Melting and evaporating

Increasing the internal energy of something won't always cause its temperature to rise. If you have some ice, which is at 0 °C, it melts and while it does so its temperature stays at 0 °C. Changes of state take place at fixed temperatures. The specific latent heat of fusion is the amount of heat put in to melt 1 kg of material (the same amount of heat is given out when the material freezes). The specific latent heat of vaporisation is the amount of heat to vaporise 1 kg of material at its boiling point. The symbol L is often used for either.

heat needed to change state

$\qquad$ = mass $\times$ specific latent heat of fusion/vaporisation

$\qquad$ = $m \times l$

Example

A   How much heat is needed to melt 300 g of ice? The specific latent heat of fusion of water is 340 000 J/kg.

heat needed to change state = $m \times l_f$

$\qquad\qquad$ = 0.3 kg $\times$ 340 000 J/kg

$\qquad\qquad$ = 102 000 J

B   The automatic cut-out on an electric kettle fails just as the water reaches boiling point. If the kettle holds 1.5 kg of water, how much energy will be wasted in boiling the kettle dry if specific latent heat of vaporisation of water is 2 300 000 J/kg.

heat needed to change state = $m \times l_v$

$\qquad\qquad$ = 1.5 kg $\times$ 2 300 000 J/kg

$\qquad\qquad$ = 3 450 000 J

$\qquad\qquad$ = 3.45 MJ

It is because the specific latent heat of vaporisation of water is so high that sweating is such a good cooling mechanism.

From this you can see that steam is very energetic so if it condenses on your skin you tend to get a serious burn.

24 Here is a question that is structured to guide you through some energy changes.

On a hot day the sun delivers energy at the rate of 800 J/s/m^2. Bob is working in the garden and wearing his new black shirt. The sun is shining full on his back.

a Approximately how much energy does he absorb from the sun each second (treat his back as a rectangle of 0.5 × 0.6 m^2)?

b How much energy is this each hour?

c Suppose he absorbs all of this energy and retains it. By how much will his temperature rise each hour? You can assume his body mass is 70 kg, and since the human body is about 80% water, treat him as if he is all water with $c = 4200$ J/kg/°C.

d To avoid this temperature rise caused by the sun he needs his rate of perspiration to increase. How much water does he need to lose each hour through perspiration? Sweat is mostly water so it has a specific latent heat of vaporisation of 2 300 000 J/kg.

Electrical energy

When electric charge flows through a component in a circuit, electrical energy is converted into some other form or forms. The amount of energy, E, converted is given by

$$E = QV \qquad \text{or} \qquad E = ItV$$

where

Q = charge which flows in coulombs
V = the potential difference across the component in volts
I = the current flow in amps
t = the time in seconds

(See Chapter 4 for more detail.)

25 How much energy is used by an electric motor run at 240 V for 1 minute if it draws a current of 7 A?

26 750 J of energy are given to a hair dryer in 3 s. If the hair dryer operates at 250 V, what current does it draw?

27 A current of 10 A is delivered to a kettle for 3 minutes. If this delivers 420 000 J, whiat potential difference does the kettle run at?

28 A torch bulb draws a current of 0.3 A from a 1.5 V battery. How long would it take to use 100 J of energy?

29 If a 1.2 V rechargeable battery stores 2700 J of electrical energy. How much longer would it run a 2.7 W bulb than a 3.1 W bulb?

Power

Sometimes we are interested not just in how much energy we need to convert for a particular purpose but also in how fast we can do it.

For example it takes 1 000 000 J to move a lift of mass 1000 kg (including its occupants) to the top of a 100 m building. (You might like to check this using PE = mgh.) Clearly the lift is better if it can do this in 100 s than in 200 s.

What we are talking about here is the *rate* of transforming energy. This is called **power**.

$$\text{power} = \frac{\text{energy transformed}}{\text{time}}$$

Or in symbols

$$P = \frac{E}{t}$$

The units of power are J/s or watts, symbol W.

Example

The power of the faster lift above is 1 000 000 J/100 s = 10 000 W. What is the power of the slower one?

What is the power of an engine that uses 12 000 J in 60 s?

$$P = \frac{E}{t}$$
$$= \frac{12\ 000\ \text{J}}{60\ \text{s}}$$
$$= 200\ \text{W}$$

Exercise

30 The human body delivers 14 000 J of energy in 2 minutes. What is the power of the body?

31 A 60 W light bulb is left on all day. How much energy is used by the bulb?

32 How long would 9 300 000 J of energy power a 600 W motor?

33 A 9000 W motor cycle runs for 30 minutes on 1.2 litres of petrol. How long would a 20 000 W motor run for on the same amount of petrol?

34 A pushbiker uses a dynamo to generate electricity for the lights on her bike. The lights are rated 3 W. If she cycles for an hour, how much energy does she use up generating electricity for her lights?

Efficiency

We have seen that energy is never destroyed. However, when we are transforming energy from one form to another, we almost always fail to convert all the energy we start with into the type of energy we require.

Examples of this include:

- In an electric motor we convert electrical energy into kinetic energy, but some energy is converted into heat in the wires.
- In a power station we convert the chemical energy of the fuel into electrical energy, but some is lost as heat in the cooling towers and as sound.

The efficiency of an energy conversion is the percentage of the energy we put in to a process which comes out in the form we require.

When energy is 'lost' in conversions it nearly always appears as heat.

$$\text{efficiency} = \frac{\text{useful energy out}}{\text{energy in}} \times 100\% \qquad \text{or}$$

$$\text{efficiency} = \frac{\text{useful power out}}{\text{power in}} \times 100\%$$

Example

A 60 W light bulb only delivers 0.3 W of light. The rest is wasted as heat. What is the efficiency of the light bulb?

$$\text{efficiency} = \frac{\text{useful power out}}{\text{power in}} \times 100\%$$

$$= \frac{0.3\ \text{W}}{60\ \text{W}} \times 100\%$$

$$= 0.5\%$$

Exercise

35 A car uses 16 800 J of chemical energy from its petrol to achieve a kinetic energy of 5200 J. What is the efficiency of the car?

36 An electric motor is only 30% efficient and is rated as using 470 W of electrical energy when working. What is the effective power output of the motor?

37 A push bike is 75% efficient and a cyclist gains 300 J of movement energy in a fast sprint. How much energy does the cyclist have to put into the bicycle?

38 A steam engine is 20% efficient at converting the chemical energy of coal into heat energy in steam. The pistons are 30% efficient at converting heat in steam into movement energy. If the steam engine has 1 200 000 J of coal fed into it how much movement energy does it gain?

Chapter 3

Motion

STARTING POINTS

- Do you understand the following terms: **speed**, **force**, **mass**? Write a sentence or two (no more) to explain what you understand by each. Then check in the glossary.

Vectors

If you are orienteering and need to know how to get to the next checkpoint, the information 'it is two miles away' is not much use. However, 'it is two miles due east' *is* helpful.

The two ideas we need to combine are distance and direction. To have one piece of information and not the other makes the task difficult if not impossible. A **vector** is a piece of information in two parts – size and direction, and it is usually shown by an arrow, see Fig 3.1.

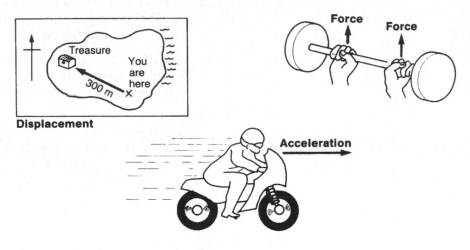

3.1 Vectors have size and direction.

A distance which also has its direction specified is called a **displacement** and is a vector quantity. Quantities which have no specified direction are called **scalars**.

1. Divide the following quantities into vectors and scalars: mass, temperature, force, volume.

Force

Forces are pushes and pulls which tend to change the motion or shape of an object. They are vectors because their direction is clearly important.

If two people are trying to push a car it is more helpful if both are pushing in the same direction. Suppose one was pushing a car with a force of 100 newtons forwards at the same time as the other was pushing it with a force of 60 newtons backwards. The **resultant** force would be 40 newtons forwards. If they both pushed forwards with the same forces, the resultant force would be 160 newtons forwards.

2 What is the resultant force in the situations in Fig 3.2?

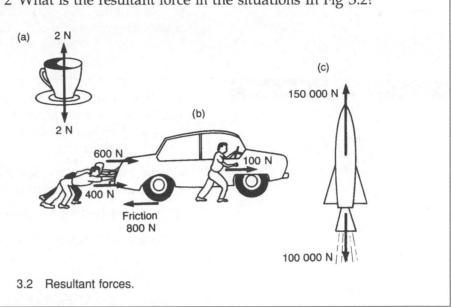

3.2   Resultant forces.

Speed and velocity

The average **speed** for a journey is the distance travelled divided by the time taken. It is a scalar quantity.

If we also specify the direction, we have a vector quantity, which we call **velocity**.

A car journey from London to Leamington covers 100 miles in two hours.

$$\text{average speed} = 100 \text{ miles}/2 \text{ hours}$$
$$= 50 \text{ miles per hour}$$

Average velocity is 50 miles per hour *in the direction of Leamington*.

3 a A cyclist covers 3 km in 6 minutes due south. What is her average velocity?
  b A runner covers 100 m in 10 seconds. What is his average speed?
  c A point on the equator rotates through 24 000 miles in 24 hours. What is its average speed?

The average velocity or speed of an object is useful if we wish to say general things about the journey, but there are times when we need to describe parts of the journey.

A car journey from Banbury to Stratford via Warwick town centre covers the 30 miles in 1 hour. The average speed of the journey is 30 miles per hour but we would expect the car to have to stop several times at roundabouts and traffic lights. This means that if 30 miles per hour is the average speed, there must have been times when the car was travelling faster than 30 miles per hour. We now need a method of calculating the speed or velocity at a particular instant.

The symbol Δ (pronounced 'delta') is a mathematical shorthand meaning 'change in'.

$$\text{velocity over a time interval} = \frac{\text{change in displacement}}{\text{change in time}} = \frac{\Delta d}{\Delta t}$$

where d represents the displacement, and t the time taken.

Remember that **displacement** is distance in a specified direction.

As Δt gets smaller, the value of average velocity becomes the instantaneous velocity at a particular instant.

4 You have just completed a charity cycling run and your friend has timed your progress through several stages of the journey. Look at the sketched map in Fig 3.3 and then work out to one significant figure:

a your average speed for the whole journey
b your average velocity over each stage.

The winner had an average speed of 0.6 km per minute.

c During which stage did the winner overtake you?

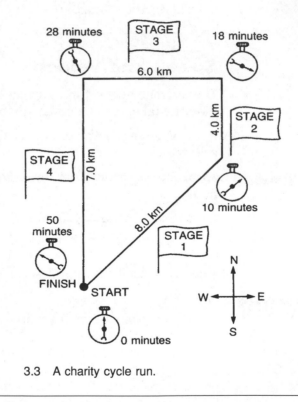

3.3 A charity cycle run.

Changing speed and velocity

We now come to another possible way of expressing average speed. If a car steadily speeds up from 10 m/s to 20 m/s during a journey, then we can describe the car's average speed as:

$$\text{average speed} = \frac{\text{finish speed} + \text{start speed}}{2}$$

Provided the car makes *no change in direction* during the journey,

$$\text{its average velocity} = \frac{v + u}{2}$$

where v represents the velocity at the end of the time interval we are considering and u the velocity at the beginning of this time period.

5 a A runner, on a straight track, steadily increases her speed from 0 m/s to 10 m/s. What is her average velocity?
  b An aircraft goes through the sound barrier by steadily increasing its speed from 250 m/s to 400 m/s. What is its average speed?
  c A car steadily increases its speed from 10 m/s to 40 m/s in 30 s. What is its average speed and how far does it travel while it is increasing its speed?

Acceleration

If the velocity of an object changes, we describe this as an **acceleration**.

$$\text{acceleration} = \frac{\text{change in velocity}}{\text{time taken}}$$

See the section in Chapter 8, Vectors, which looks at change in direction.

There are two points to note here.

- Since velocity is a vector, a change in velocity could be a change in speed or a change in direction, or both.
- If an object is slowing down, then its acceleration is negative, and is sometimes called deceleration.

In symbol form there are two ways of expressing the acceleration of an object:

1) average acceleration, $\quad a = \dfrac{v - u}{t}$

  $v =$ finish velocity
  $u =$ start velocity
  $t =$ time taken

2) acceleration, $\quad a = \dfrac{\Delta v}{\Delta t}$

  $\Delta v =$ change in velocity
  $\Delta t =$ change in time

In the same way as before, the smaller Δt is, the closer this becomes to the instantaneous acceleration.

The performances of cars are often quoted as their times to go from 0–25 m/s (0–60 mph). This is supposed to tell us something useful about the car but what does it mean?

A car, travelling in a straight line, accelerates from 0 m/s to 25 m/s in 12.5 s. What is its acceleration?

$$a = \frac{v - u}{t} \quad \text{where } v = 25 \text{ m/s}, \ u = 0 \text{ m/s and } t = 12.5 \text{ s}$$

m/s/s (metres per second per second) can also be written (m/s)/s or m/s².

$a = 25 - 0$ m/s/12.5 s
$a = 25/12.5$ m/s/s
$a = 2$ m/s/s

This means that the car speeds up by 2 metres per second, every second.

6 a Work out the accelerations of vehicles on straight tracks, which
speed up from 0–25 m/s in these times:
i lorry, 25 s   ii bus, 20 s   iii teacher's car, 15 s
iv sports car, 8 s   v motorcycle, 3 s
b A pushbike accelerates from 0 to 6 m/s in 2 s on a straight
road. What is the acceleration of the pushbike? Compare this
with the acceleration of the motor-driven vehicles in the first
part of the question.
c If a pushbike's acceleration is so great, why do we use motor-
driven vehicles?
d A falling object accelerates at 10 m/s/s. If we start to measure
its fall when its speed is 13 m/s, how fast is it going 8 s after
this?

Equations of motion

We now have several equations which we can use to describe what is
happening to an object while it is moving. Each equation is like a
colour on a painting palette. We can outline a picture using one colour
but the more colours we have, the better we are able to enhance the
picture with detail.

A runner, on a straight track, accelerates steadily from the
starting blocks during a race at 2 m/s/s. The runner accelerates for
5 s. What is his velocity when he finishes accelerating? What is his
average velocity? How far does he travel in the 5 seconds?

We are dealing with a steady acceleration, so $a = \dfrac{v - u}{t}$

Filling in the values in the equation, $2 \text{ m/s/s} = \dfrac{(v - 0) \text{ m/s}}{5 \text{ s}}$

This gives us an answer of $2 = v/5$, so $v = 10$ m/s when he finishes
accelerating. We now know the change in velocity.

$$\text{average velocity} = \frac{v + u}{2}$$
$$= \frac{(10 + 0) \text{ m/s}}{2}$$

average velocity $= 5$ m/s while he is accelerating.

The acceleration takes 5 seconds, so now we can work out the distance
he travels from the equation:

$$\text{average velocity} = d/t$$
$$5 \text{ m/s} = \frac{d}{5 \text{ seconds}}$$
$$d = 25 \text{ m}$$

So the runner travels 25 m while accelerating.

7 a A stone is dropped from a cliff. It accelerates towards the sea at
10 m/s/s. If it starts from rest and falls for 3 s before hitting
the sea, how fast is it travelling when it hits the sea?
b What is the average velocity of the falling stone?
c How tall is the cliff?

8 A racing car accelerates steadily from rest at the start line at 6
m/s/s for 10 s. What is its average velocity during acceleration?
How far does it travel during acceleration? Assume the car is on a
straight track.

Graphs

Graphs are a neat way to summarise and present data. A glance at the shape of the line can tell you how two variables relate. Graphs, however, contain more information than this if you know how to obtain it.

For moving objects we can plot distance–time or velocity–time graphs.

Fig 3.4 is a **velocity–time** graph for an object moving with steady velocity. Its acceleration is zero.

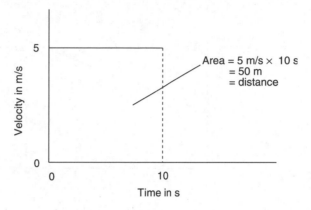

3.4   A velocity–time graph.

The object was travelling at 5 m/s for 10 s so how far did it travel?

$$\text{distance} = \text{velocity} \times \text{time}$$
$$= 5 \text{ m/s} \times 10 \text{ s}$$
$$= 50 \text{ m}$$

We have just multiplied one side of a rectangle by the other, so we have calculated its area.

So we can say:

distance travelled = area under the velocity–time graph.

If we plot a **distance–time** graph for uniform velocity it looks like this.

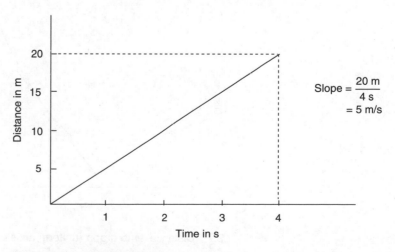

3.5   A distance–time graph.

Since the same distance is covered each second the line is straight. The gradient (or slope) of a graph is how steep it is – the vertical rise/horizontal distance.

The gradient of this graph is 20 m/4 s = 5 m/s and this is the velocity.
So we can say:

gradient of a distance–time graph = velocity.

Now let's tackle something a little more demanding. Fig 3.6 shows the variation of velocity with time for a uniformly accelerated object. We will use this graph to generalise the result from our first graph.

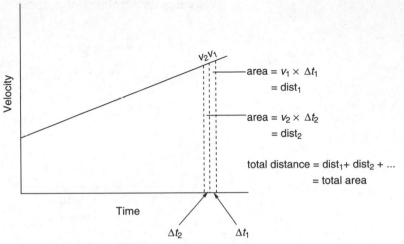

3.6   Velocity–time graph (uniform acceleration).

Think about the small time interval Δt_1. The velocity during this time was approximately v_1. So the distance travelled in Δt_1, (velocity × time) = $v_1 \times \Delta t_1$. Similarly the distance travelled in time Δt_2 is $v_2 \times \Delta t_2$. But $v \times \Delta t$ is the area of a strip. So to find the total distance we would need to find the area of each strip and add them all together. Again we see that distance = area under the velocity–time graph. If we make the strips narrower and narrower the approximation gets better and better.

We often use the symbol d to indicate a small part of something.

Fig 3.7 is a distance–time graph for an object which is accelerating uniformly. Since the object is travelling faster and faster it is covering

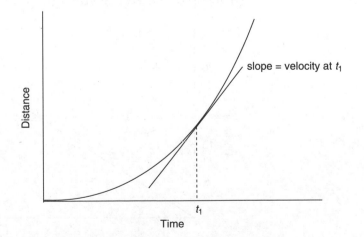

3.7   Distance–time graph (uniform acceleration).

A tangent is a straight line drawn touching a curve at a particular point.

more and more ground in successive time intervals so the graph gets steeper and steeper. You could find the velocity at any time by working out the gradient. To do this you have to draw the tangent to the curve and then work out the slope of the tangent.

Example

Fig 3.8 shows how the velocity of a cyclist varied over a 20 s time period.

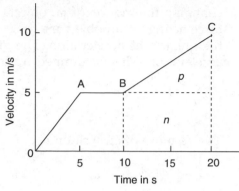

3.8   Velocity–time graph for cyclist.

a What can you say about the acceleration during the first 5 s?

  The acceleration was uniform as it is a straight-line graph.

    acceleration = change in velocity/time taken

$$= \frac{(5 - 0) \text{ m/s}}{5 \text{ s}}$$

$$= 1 \text{ m/s/s}$$

b How far did the cyclist travel in the first 5 s?

  distance travelled = area under graph from 0 s to 5 s

  the area of a triangle $= \frac{1}{2}$ base × height

    distance = area $= \frac{1}{2} \times 5$ s × 5 m/s

$$= 12.5 \text{ m}$$

c How far did the cyclist travel during the final 10 s?

  distance = area under graph from 10 s to 20 s

$$= \text{area } n + \text{area } p$$

$$= \text{area of rectangle} + \text{area of triangle}$$

$$= 5 \text{ m/s} \times 10 \text{ s} + (\tfrac{1}{2} \times 15 \text{ m/s} \times 10 \text{ s})$$

$$= 50 \text{ m} + 25 \text{ m}$$

$$= 75 \text{ m}$$

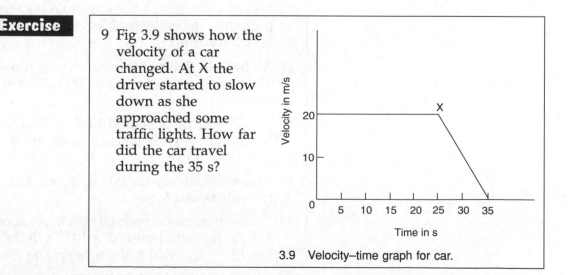
Exercise

9 Fig 3.9 shows how the velocity of a car changed. At X the driver started to slow down as she approached some traffic lights. How far did the car travel during the 35 s?

3.9   Velocity–time graph for car.

Force and acceleration

We saw at the beginning of the chapter that a force has the effect of changing the motion of an object. More precisely, an unbalanced force acting on an object makes it accelerate. The greater the force, the greater the acceleration. The greater the mass, the smaller the acceleration. This is summed up in the following equation:

$$a = \frac{F}{m}$$

This is more often written as

The equation $F = ma$ is a mathematical statement of Newton's Second Law of Motion.

$$F = ma$$

where F is the unbalanced force acting on the object in newtons (N)
m is its mass in kg
a is the acceleration in m/s/s

It is important to realise that F represents the *unbalanced* force on the object. An object may have several forces on it – only the unbalanced or **resultant** force causes it to accelerate. You will have at least two forces acting on you at the moment – gravity pulling you down and your chair pushing you upwards. These are of the same size and in opposite directions so they cancel. There is no unbalanced force so you do not accelerate.

Example

A 1000 kg car, travelling along a straight track, accelerates from rest to 25 m/s in 10 s. What is the unbalanced force on the car?

$$a = \frac{v - u}{t}$$

$$a = \frac{(25 - 0)\ \text{m/s}}{10\ \text{s}} = 2.5\ \text{m/s/s}$$

$$F = ma$$

$$F = 1000\ \text{kg} \times 2.5\ \text{m/s/s} = 2500\ \text{N}$$

Exercise

In questions 10 to 16, assume travel is in a straight line.

10 A cyclist accelerates from rest to 6 m/s in 2 s. Her mass (including the cycle) is 60 kg. With what force is she pushing herself forward?

11 An Intercity 125 train accelerates from rest to 40 m/s in 40 s. The train has a mass of 200 000 kg. What is the accelerating force?

12 A force of 2000 N is used to slow down a 1000 kg car from 30 m/s to a stop. What is its acceleration? How long will it take to stop?

13 An aircraft of mass 20 000 kg accelerates at 11 m/s/s. What is the unbalanced force?

14 An electron inside your television set accelerates from rest to 3×10^7 m/s in a time of 1×10^{-9} s. If the mass of an electron is 6×10^{-31} kg, what is the accelerating force on the electron?

Combining equations of motion in a straight line

So far we have seen several different equations to describe the movements of objects travelling in a straight line. It is possible to combine two or more of these equations to make them more convenient to use. We shall use the symbols:

v = final velocity s = distance travelled a = steady acceleration

u = initial velocity t = time taken

If an object accelerates with constant acceleration, a, in a straight line, then its velocity increases by an amount, a, every second, so that after t seconds its velocity has increased by an amount $a \times t$. If it started with a velocity u, its final velocity will be $u + (a \times t)$. This is the first equation of motion

$$\mathbf{v = u + at} \qquad (1)$$

Now suppose that, instead of knowing that the object accelerated for a *time*, t, we know that the object accelerated over a *distance*, s. What is the equation for its final velocity? The equation connecting s with the average velocity is

$$\text{average velocity} = \frac{s}{t} = \frac{u + v}{2}$$

so the time taken, t, is $t = 2s/(u + v)$.

Replacing t in the equation (1) with this expression gives

$$\mathbf{v = u + 2as/(u + v)}$$

Multiplying this out gives us

$$v(u + v) = u(u + v) + 2as$$
$$\text{or} \quad vu + v^2 = u^2 + uv + 2as$$

which gives us the second equation of motion:

$$\mathbf{v^2 = u^2 + 2as} \qquad (2)$$

Finally, if an object started with velocity u, and accelerated for time t, how far did it travel? Here we can use equation (1) together with the definition of average velocity:

$$v = u + at \quad \text{and} \quad \text{average velocity} = \frac{s}{t} = \frac{u + v}{2}$$

So,
$$s = \frac{(u + v)t}{2}$$

Since $v = u + at$,
$$s = \frac{(u + u + at)t}{2}$$
$$s = \frac{(2u + at)t}{2}$$

and this gives us the last equation of motion:

$$\mathbf{s = ut + \tfrac{1}{2}at^2} \qquad (3)$$

Exercise

Use the above equations of motion to tackle the following questions.

15 A ball is dropped from a height of 16 m. If the ball starts from rest, how long does it take to hit the ground? (Assume it accelerates at 10 m/s/s.)

16 A motorbike accelerates to a speed of 12 m/s, starting from rest, over a distance of 36 m. If the bike has a mass of 250 kg, what force is provided by the engine?

17 A parachutist freefalls for 7 s. If he leaves the plane from rest, how fast is he going at the end of his free fall (assume he accelerates at 10 m/s^2)? Do you think the assumption is a reasonable one?

Momentum

When an object is moving towards you, the concern you have for your safety depends on how fast the object is moving and how massive it is.

You would certainly step out of the way of a lorry, whereas you might not notice a fly moving at the same speed. The lorry's extra mass means it has greater **momentum** and so is harder to stop.

The momentum, p, of any moving object of mass, m, and velocity, v, is given by

momentum = mass × velocity

$$p = mv$$

Since velocity is a vector quantity, so is momentum. The units of momentum are those of mass multiplied by those of velocity so the usual ones are kg m/s.

Example

A 0.01 kg bullet travels at 500 m/s. What is its momentum?

$p = mv$

$p = 0.01 \text{ kg} \times 500 \text{ m/s}$

$p = 5 \text{ kg m/s}$

This is the same as the momentum of a 1 kg brick travelling at 5 m/s. Check that you agree with this.

Exercise

18 a Calculate the momentum of a 70 kg runner travelling at 10 m/s.
   b If a car has a momentum of 12 000 kg m/s and a mass of 1000 kg, how fast is it going?
   c A cyclist travelling at 12 m/s has a momentum of 960 kg m/s. What is the mass of the cyclist plus cycle?
   d A 0.2 kg cricket ball is thrown at 40 m/s. What is the momentum of the ball?
   e If an aircraft has a mass of 50 000 kg and is travelling at 400 m/s, what is its momentum?

Collisions and momentum

Whenever a moving object hits another object then all the momentum before the collision is still there after the collision even if different objects actually have the momentum. We say that the momentum is **conserved**. This enables us to do calculations about moving objects. For example a forensic scientist might be able to calculate the velocity at which a car accident took place. Snooker players work with momentum instinctively; we might have to do calculations like those in the example. To keep things simple we shall assume that all the collisions take place in a straight line.

A ball of mass 3 kg with a velocity of 2 m/s collides head on with a second ball of mass 2 kg and all the momentum is passed on. What velocity does the second ball move off with if it is initially at rest?

mv before collision $= 3$ kg $\times 2$ m/s $= 6$ kg m/s

Since momentum is conserved,

mv after collision $= 6$ kg m/s $= 2$ kg $\times ?$

So the velocity of the second ball must be 3 m/s, in the same direction.

19 a A car of mass 1000 kg with a velocity of 25 m/s hits a bus of mass 10 000 kg. Assuming all the momentum is passed to the bus, how fast does the bus travel after the collision?
   b A tennis racket of mass 1 kg with a velocity of 20 m/s hits a tennis ball of mass 0.1 kg. If the ball leaves the racket at 40 m/s, then calculate:
      i) the momentum of the tennis racket before the collision
      ii) the momentum of the ball after the collision
      iii) the momentum the racket still has after the collision.
      iv) the velocity of the racket after the collision.

20 A hockey stick of mass 1.5 kg hits a hockey ball of mass 0.25 kg. After the collision the ball moves with a velocity of 30 m/s and the hockey stick stops. What was the speed of the hockey stick before the collision?

More about momentum

Another way of stating the law of conservation of momentum is that the total momentum of a closed system cannot change. A closed system is simply one to which nothing is added or taken away. It could be a pair of snooker balls, the Earth, or the whole universe. Momentum is a vector quantity. Thus, an object moving in one direction has the negative of the amount of momentum that an identical object has moving in the opposite direction.

If we throw a 1 kg brick vertically upwards at 10 m/s, the brick has a momentum, p, given by

$p = mv$

$p = 1$ kg $\times 10$ m/s

$p = 10$ kg m/s

The system of the brick and the Earth originally had no momentum so where has this momentum come from?

The answer is that the Earth has moved off in the opposite direction with an equal and opposite momentum, so that the total momentum of the Earth plus ball system is zero, as it was before we threw the ball.

How fast does the Earth move as a result? The Earth's momentum must also be 10 kg m/s in the opposite direction. The mass of the Earth is 1×10^{24} kg. Hence,

$$10 \text{ kg m/s} = 1 \times 10^{24} \text{ kg} \times v$$

So the velocity of the Earth is 1×10^{-23} m/s in the opposite direction to that in which the ball was thrown. At this velocity it would take the Earth over 300 000 years to cover a distance equal to the width of an atom! (an atom is about 1.0×10^{-10} m in diameter). No wonder we do not notice this movement!

Exercise

21 All 5×10^9 people on the Earth gather on the Isle of Man. At an agreed time they all jump up so their maximum upward velocity is 20 m/s. The average mass of each person is 60 kg. If the Earth has a mass of 1×10^{24} kg, how fast does it move downwards?

22 A gun is used to fire a 0.01 kg bullet at 1000 m/s.
    a The gun has a mass of 2 kg. How fast is it propelled backwards?
    b If the individual firing the gun has a mass of 78 kg, how fast is he or she propelled backwards?

23 In some films, actors are seen being thrown backwards by the impact of a bullet. Yet the person firing the gun is unaffected. Explain why this is not possible.

Direction and momentum

Some of the situations we have been looking at are examples of 'explosions'. In each case the same amount of momentum moves off in opposite directions; for the brick and the Earth that is 10 kg m/s each. Now since there is no momentum before the 'explosion', there should be no momentum after. We have dealt with this by talking about one lot of momentum cancelling out the other. The only way two equal numbers can cancel is if one is positive and the other negative. So mathematically this is what we do with momentum. If the brick had $+10$ kg m/s then the Earth had -10 kg m/s. When these are added we get zero.

$$+10 \text{ kg m/s} + (-10 \text{ kg m/s}) = +10 \text{ kg m/s} - 10 \text{ kg m/s} = 0$$

When using vectors (see Chapter 8) the negative sign is used to denote opposite direction. If you put the negative signs in at the start of a calculation then you can forget about directions and leave it to the maths to sort things out.

Example

A car and a lorry collide head on and stick together. The car was travelling at 30 m/s and the lorry 20 m/s. The mass of the car was 1000 kg and the lorry 3000 kg. What is the total momentum of the system and in which direction will they move after the collision?

Take the direction of the car to be positive and that of the lorry to be negative. (You could do it the other way and check that you end up with the same answer.)

Before

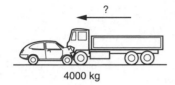

30 m/s

- 20 m/s

1000 kg

3000 kg

After

?

4000 kg

3.10 A head-on collision.

Before collision:

$$\text{car's momentum} = \text{mass} \times \text{velocity}$$
$$= m_c \times v_c$$
$$= 1000 \text{ kg} \times 30 \text{ m/s}$$
$$= 30\,000 \text{ kg m/s}$$

$$\text{lorry's momentum} = \text{mass} \times \text{velocity}$$
$$= m_l \times v_l$$
$$= 3000 \text{ kg} \times -20 \text{ m/s}$$
$$= -60\,000 \text{ kg m/s}$$

$$\text{total momentum} = \text{car's momentum} + \text{lorry's momentum}$$
$$= 30\,000 + (-60\,000)$$
$$= 30\,000 - 60\,000$$
$$= -30\,000 \text{ kg m/s}$$

The momentum before = momentum after, so

$$\text{momentum after} = -30\,000 \text{ kg m/s}$$

Since momentum is negative they move in the direction of the lorry.

Since momentum = mass × velocity and the combined mass of lorry and car is 4000 kg, we can find the velocity they move with after the collision.

$$-30\,000 \text{ kg m/s} = 4000 \text{ kg} \times v$$
$$v = -7.5 \text{ m/s}$$

What we are doing here is dealing *explicitly* with the vector nature of momentum. If, however, you feel uncomfortable with this use of signs, then you can continue with our original approach.

The idea of conservation of momentum can be used in propulsion systems. For example, you could load up a boat with rocks – big ones would be best – and stand throwing them out the back as hard as you could. As you throw each rock backwards, it gains some momentum in that direction. The boat must get the same amount of momentum in the opposite direction, so it starts to move forward. It seems a silly idea, but this is essentially what happens in a jet ski; it squirts water backwards at high velocity, instead of rocks, so that the jet ski moves forwards. Rocket propulsion systems operate in the same way. Very hot gas is ejected at the back at very high speed. The momentum the gas carries away is matched by the momentum gained by the rocket in the forward direction. Our system here has developed from using large particles at low speeds to smaller and smaller particles at higher and higher speeds.

Example

A spacecraft has a mass of 30 000 kg and it burns fuel at a rate of 15 kg each second. This hot gas leaves the back of the spacecraft at 3000 m/s. If the rockets are ignited and run for 3 seconds by how much will the spacecraft's speed increase?

Conservation principle tells us (considering magnitudes only):

momentum gained by gas = momentum gained by craft:

momentum gained by gas = mass burned × velocity

In 3 s it burns 45 kg of fuel

$$\text{momentum gained by gas} = 45 \text{ kg} \times 3000 \text{ m/s}$$
$$= 135\ 000 \text{ kg m/s}$$

$$\text{momentum gained by craft} = \text{mass} \times \text{velocity gain}$$
$$135\ 000 \text{ kg m/s} = 30\ 000 \text{ kg} \times \text{velocity gain}$$

Divide both sides by 30 000

$$\text{velocity gain} = \frac{135\ 000 \text{ kg m/s}}{30\ 000 \text{ kg}}$$
$$= 4.5 \text{ m/s}$$

Impulse

If you play a sport in which you hit a ball, for example tennis, golf or football, you will know that for maximum effect you need to 'follow through'. The physical reason for this is really quite simple. On following through you keep the force acting on the ball for longer so it has a greater effect. Let's look more carefully at the physics of this.

As our starting point let's take Newton's Second Law:

the unbalanced force = mass × acceleration
$$F = m \times a$$

But acceleration is the change in velocity per second, so we can write

$$a = \frac{v - u}{t}$$

where v is final velocity, u is initial velocity and t is time.

We can now put this in the equation in place of a

$$F = \frac{m(v - u)}{t}$$

If we now multiply both sides of the equation by t we get

$$F \times t = m(v - u)$$

Now the bracket means that everything inside is multiplied by m. If we do that we end up with,

$$F \times t = mv - mu$$

mv is the momentum at the end of time t; mu is the momentum at the start of time t; so

$$mv - mu = \text{change of momentum}$$

and we can now write

$$F \times t = \text{change of momentum}$$

This equation is saying that if you double the time for which the force acts, you will double the change in the momentum. In other words you double the effect of the force. If you double the force, you double its effect. The expression $F \times t$ is a measure of the effect the force has and so has been given a special name;

$$F \times t = \textbf{impulse}$$

A note on units: impulse is force × time and so has units of newton seconds (N s). Impulse, however, equals change of momentum which has units of kg m/s. This means that N s are equivalent to kg m/s. By convention we use N s when talking about impulse.

Example

In a class demonstration, a physics teacher kicked a stationary football and measured the time of contact with the ball to be 0.03 seconds. The ball had a mass of 0.3 kg. After the kick, the ball travelled at 10 m/s. What average force acted on the ball during the kick?

$$F \times t = \text{change in momentum}$$

$$\text{momentum after kick} = 0.3 \text{ kg} \times 10 \text{ m/s}$$
$$= 3 \text{ kg m/s}$$

$F = ma$

Considering units

$$N = kg \text{ m/s}^2$$

Multiplyng both sides by s

$$N \text{ s} = kg \text{ m/s}$$

showing that the units are equivalent

This is the change in momentum as the ball had no initial momentum and so equals the impulse

$$F \times t = 3 \text{ kg m/s}$$
$$F \times 0.03 \text{ s} = 3 \text{ kg m/s}$$
$$F = \frac{3 \text{ kg m/s}}{0.03 \text{ s}}$$
$$= 100 \text{ kg m/s}^2$$
$$= 100 \text{ N}$$

Seat belts in cars represent an application of the impulse relation. In a collision, a car can stop in a very short time interval and this means a very large force is acting to change the momentum. The intention with seat belts is to ensure passengers take a little longer to stop. This is achieved if the belt stretches. It can then apply a smaller force over a longer time to bring about the same momentum change.

Example

A car is travelling at 15 m/s and collides with a stationary lorry. The car comes to a halt in 70 ms. If the mass of the car is 1000 kg, what retarding force acts on the car?

$$\text{impulse} = \text{change in momentum}$$
$$F \times t = \text{change in momentum}$$

change in momentum $= m \times v$ (car has no momentum when it stops).

$$\text{change in momentum} = 1000 \text{ kg} \times 15 \text{ m/s}$$
$$= 15\,000 \text{ kg m/s}$$
$$F \times t = 15\,000 \text{ kg m/s}$$
$$F \times 0.07 \text{ s} = 15\,000 \text{ kg m/s}$$
$$F = \frac{15\,000 \text{ kg m/s}}{0.07 \text{ s}}$$
$$F = 2.1 \times 10^5 \text{ N}$$

In a crash like this the passenger starts to move forward 30 ms after impact and is stopped by the seat belt 80 ms after impact. If the driver has a mass of 70 kg, what retarding force acts on her?

$$\text{time to bring the driver to rest} = 80 - 30 \text{ ms}$$
$$= 50 \text{ ms}$$
$$\text{change in momentum} = 70 \text{ kg} \times 15 \text{ m/s}$$
$$= 1050 \text{ kg/ m/s}$$
$$F \times t = 1050 \text{ kg m/s}$$
$$F \times 0.05 \text{ s} = 1050 \text{ kg m/s}$$
$$F = \frac{1050 \text{ kg m/s}}{0.05 \text{ s}}$$
$$= 2.1 \times 10^4 \text{ N}$$

This is quite a large force. It is equivalent to the weight of a small elephant and the collision is, in fact, low speed (30 mph). To survive high-speed collisions air bags are needed.

Exercise

24 A car of mass 1200 kg collided when travelling at 20 m/s. The car was brought rest in 90 ms. What was the average retarding force?

Impulse problem

Every winter the wind blows down at least one fence panel in Bob's back garden. It amuses the neighbours because it doesn't happen to them. He decided to work out just what force was doing the damage, using the impulse equation.

Each panel in the fence is about 2 m × 2 m. The last time the fence suffered, the wind was gusting to 70 mph, which is approximately 30 m/s. Looking at the diagram you can see how much air hit the fence each second; all of the air in the box 30 m long by 2 m in width and 2 m high. So

$$\text{volume of air hitting per second} = 30 \text{ m} \times 2 \text{ m} \times 2 \text{ m}$$
$$= 120 \text{ m}^3$$

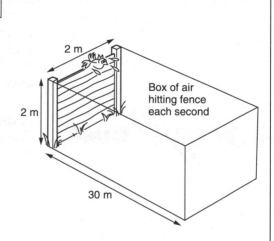

3.11　The force on Bob's fence.

To find the mass of air hitting the fence each second we need to multiply the volume of air by the density of air (1.0 kg/m^3).

$$\text{mass of air hitting per second} = 120 \text{ m}^3 \times 1.0 \text{ kg/m}^3$$
$$= 120 \text{ kg}$$

If we assume all this air stops then the momentum transferred each second is mass of air × velocity on collision

$$\text{momentum lost by air} = mv$$
$$= 120 \text{ kg} \times 40 \text{ m/s}$$
$$= 4800 \text{ kg m/s}$$

This then is equal to the impulse acting on both the air and the fence panel

$$F \times t = 4800 \text{ kg m/s}$$

We have been looking at what happens in a second so $t = 1$ s

So the force on the panel is 4800 N.

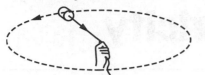

Centripetal force –
the bung moves in a circle.

3.12   The centripetal force needed to keep the bung in circular motion is supplied by the tension in the string.

Circular motion

Circular motion is a topic where particular care is needed. This is because there is a serious difference between the facts and what your senses seem to tell you. Imagine swinging a rubber bung around your head on a string. You would feel a force pulling out on your hand and you automatically associated this with rotation. But suppose the bung were swinging you around on the end of a piece of string. You would now feel the string pull you towards the bung, i.e. inwards, towards the centre of the circle. It is this inward force which is needed for circular motion and it is called the **centripetal force**. Anything moving in a circle is doing so because a centripetal force is acting on it.

In some cases it is difficult to identify what provides the centripetal force. In the case of the bung it was the tension in the string.

Exercise

> 25 What provides the centripetal force in these situations?
>
>   a a satellite in Earth orbit
>   b a car taking a corner
>   c a passenger sitting in the middle of the *smooth* back seat of a car taking a corner.

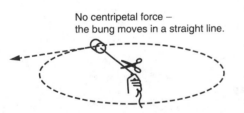

No centripetal force –
the bung moves in a straight line.

3.13   When there is no centripetal force, for example when the string is cut, the bung no longer performs circular motion but moves in a straight line.

If the centripetal force is removed then there is no reason for the body to move in the circle and so it resumes straight line motion and starts off on a tangent to the circle.

This is what is happening to a car when it skids on an icy corner. Under these conditions the frictional force is so small that it can be considered zero and the car continues to move in a straight line.

Chapter 4

Current electricity

STARTING POINTS

- Do you understand the following terms: **conductor, insulator, electron, electric circuit, series circuit, parallel circuit**? Write a sentence or two (no more) to explain what you mean by each term, then check in the glossary.

- You should know these circuit symbols:

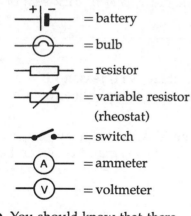

  = battery

  = bulb

  = resistor

  = variable resistor (rheostat)

  = switch

  = ammeter

  = voltmeter

- You should know that there are two types of electric charge – positive and negative. Like charges repel and unlike charges attract.

A mental picture of electricity

Electrical effects are caused by minute negatively charged particles called electrons that cannot be seen and which interact through an invisible force. Fortunately, we can often compare electricity to something that we are more familiar with – the behaviour of water as it flows through pipes. Scientists often use mental models like this to help them understand things but they have to be aware that such comparisons are not always exact.

Static electricity

Static electricity is what makes dry hair crackle when you comb it and it is what attracts small pieces of paper to a plastic ruler after it has been rubbed with a dry cloth. We can produce a larger quantity of static electricity with a Van de Graaff generator (see Fig 4.1). This

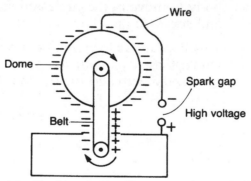

4.1 The Van de Graaff generator 'pumps' charge on to its dome.

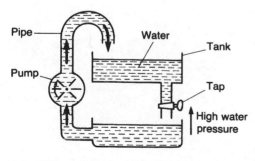

4.2 This tank and pump system is comparable to a Van de Graaff generator.

machine has a rubber belt, rather like a conveyor belt, which carries electric charge on to its dome. There is an analogy between a Van de Graaff generator and the water pump and tank shown in Fig 4.2.

The volume of water stored in the tank is analogous to the electric charge stored by the dome of the Van de Graaff generator. Electric charge is simply a measurement of a quantity of electrons and is measured in **coulombs**. It compares to a quantity of water measured in gallons. One coulomb consists of about 6×10^{18} electrons, so each electron has charge of about 1.6×10^{-19} coulombs.

Pumping the water into the tank builds up a pressure. The electrical equivalent of this is the potential, measured in volts, and sometimes loosely called 'voltage'. Thus we can now visualise why sparks fly off the dome of the Van de Graaff. The potential difference between the dome and the surroundings builds up as more and more electrons are pushed on to the dome. Eventually this becomes high enough to break down the insulation of the air and cause electrons to flow out of the dome as a spark. This is similar to the pressure of the water inside the tank in Fig 4.2 becoming so great that a pressure relief valve on the tank opens and water escapes.

Current electricity

Here, too, you may find the analogy between the flow of electric charge and flow of water helpful, see Fig 4.3.

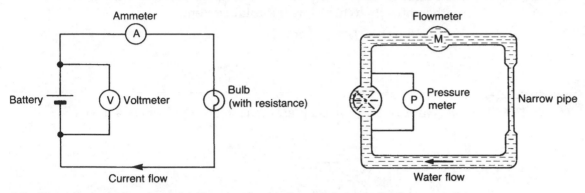

4.3   There is an analogy between the electric circuit and the water circuit.

The battery drives electrons around the circuit and through a component which resists the flow. It is comparable to a pump driving water through pipework which includes a narrow section.

An ammeter measures the rate at which charge flows through the circuit. It corresponds to a water flowmeter.

A voltmeter measures the difference in electrical potential (potential difference) between two points in the circuit – in this case either side of the battery. This is like a water pressure meter.

Electric current

Electric current (symbol I) is the rate of flow of electric charge (symbol Q). It is measured in coulombs (symbol C) per second or amperes – usually shortened to amps (symbol A). One amp is a flow of charge of one coulomb per second. Hence,

$$I = \frac{Q}{t}$$

where I is current in amps
Q is charge in coulombs
t is time in seconds

So a current of 1 amp is flowing along a wire if 1 coulomb (about 6×10^{18} electrons) flows through that wire every second.

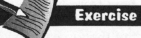

Exercise

1   A current of two amps flows through a light bulb. How much charge flows through the light bulb in 30 seconds?

2   The charge flowing from a battery every five seconds is 10 C. What current is flowing?

Currents around a circuit

Electric charge is not used up when it flows around a circuit. In a circuit like the one in Fig 4.3, we will get the same value for the current wherever we put the ammeter. This is because there is only one possible path for the charge to take, and none of it can escape.

In a circuit like the one in Fig 4.4, however, there are three paths for the current. When the current gets to point P, it must split into three. However, as no current can escape, the sum of the currents flowing in each branch must be equal to the original current. Or, expressed mathematically, where I_t is the total current,

$$I_t = I_1 + I_2 + I_3$$

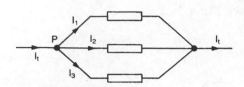
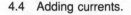

4.4   Adding currents.

Exercise

3 Work out the missing ammeter readings in Figs 4.5 to 4.7.

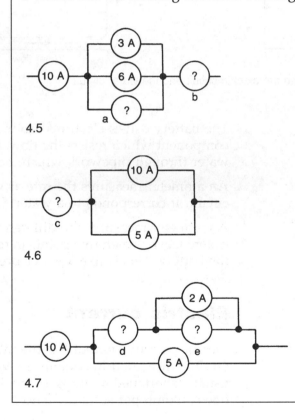

4.5

4.6

4.7

Potential difference

An electric current will flow around a circuit if there is a difference in electrical potential between two points in it. This is rather like saying that water will flow if there is a height difference between two points on the ground. The water will flow from high to low. Electric charge will flow from a high electrical potential to a low one. Electric potential measures the amount of energy that a charge has at any point. So charge will flow from a high energy point to a lower one if it is free to move. It is the **potential difference** (symbol V) between the two points which matters. This is often loosely called the voltage since it is measured in volts (symbol V).

If we have a positive charge and it moves from positive to negative, it will move of its own accord and *give up* energy. If it moves from negative to positive, it will have to be pushed by some external force and it will *gain* energy.

Definition of the volt

The potential difference between two points is 1 volt if 1 joule of energy is transformed when 1 coulomb of charge is moved between the two points. So,

1 volt = 1 joule/coulomb

This is a very important statement indeed. It tells us that there will be an energy change of 1 joule for every coulomb that moves through a potential difference of 1 volt. Expressed mathematically, the energy change, W, of a charge, Q, as it moves through a potential difference of V volts is given by,

$$W = QV$$

Example

An electric heater is switched on for one minute. Fifteen coulombs of charge moves through a potential difference of 240 V. How much heat energy is produced?

$$W = QV$$
$$W = 15\,\text{C} \times 240\,\text{V} = 3600\,\text{J}$$

Heat energy produced $= 3600$ J

Exercise

4 How much energy is transformed if:

a 1 C moves through a potential difference of 10 V?
b 12 C moves through a potential difference of 2 V?
c 1 electron moves through a potential difference of 10 V?

The television tube

A television screen emits light energy due to speeding electrons hitting the phosphor particles coating the face of the tube (Fig 4.8). The energy transformed into light comes from the kinetic energy of the electrons. The electrons produced by the electron gun are accelerated towards the screen due to the attraction of the high positive potential there. The greater the potential, the greater the acceleration, and the higher the final velocity and kinetic energy the electrons have as they hit the screen.

The tube designer needs a way to determine what potential difference is required between the electron and the screen to give electrons the levels of kinetic energy needed for normal operation of a TV tube.

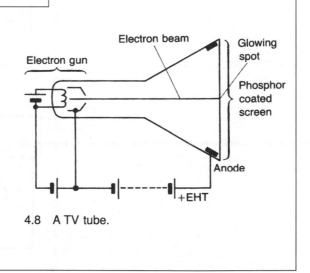

4.8   A TV tube.

Example

The potential difference between the screen and the electron gun of a TV tube is 15 000 V. How much kinetic energy does each electron have as it hits the screen?

$$W = QV$$

where W = energy given to electron
V = the potential difference across the tube
Q = the charge of an electron

$$W = 1.6 \times 10^{-19}\,\text{C} \times 15\,000\,\text{V} = 2.4 \times 10^{-15}\,\text{J}$$

The kinetic energy of the electron as it hits the screen is 2.4×10^{-15} J

Exercise

5 See if you can calculate the velocity of the electron just before it hits the screen. Hint: rearrange $KE = \frac{1}{2}mv^2$, see Chapter 2. The mass of the electron is 0.9×10^{-30} kg.

Potential differences around a circuit

Potential differences between different points in a circuit add up. So in Fig 4.9, the total potential difference, $V_t = V_1 + V_2 + V_3$. This is just like saying that the heights in Fig 4.10 add up.

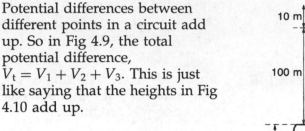

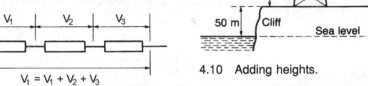

$$V_t = V_1 + V_2 + V_3$$

4.10   Adding heights.

4.9   Adding potential differences.

Exercise

6 Work out the missing voltmeter readings in Figs 4.11 to 4.13.

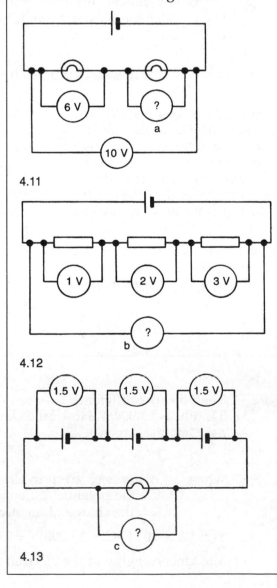

4.11

4.12

4.13

Resistance

Resistance (symbol R), measured in ohms (symbol Ω), is a measure of how difficult it is for the current to flow through a particular component (a resistor) in the circuit. The greater the resistance, the smaller the current flow (for a given potential difference). A part of a circuit with a high resistance is rather like a narrow pipe in a plumbing system which the water will find difficult to pass through. A given length of narrow pipe will have a smaller volume of water flowing through it than a wide one for the same pressure.

Exercise

> 7 Would you expect thick or thin wire (of the same metal) to have the higher resistance?

Most electric circuits have several components so it is useful to be able to calculate the overall effect that several resistors have when they are used in combination.

Resistors in series

In a series circuit, the current must flow through each component in succession, see Fig 4.14.

The rule for combining resistances in this case is very simple. The total resistance,
$R_t = R_1 + R_2 + R_3$

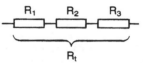

4.14   Resistors in series.

Resistors in parallel

In a parallel circuit, there are two or more alternative paths for the current which will split itself amongst the alternative branches, see Fig 4.15.

The rule here is not so simple! It is

$$\frac{1}{R_t} = \frac{1}{R_1} + \frac{1}{R_2} + \frac{1}{R_3}$$

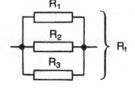

4.15   Resistors in parallel.

What is the total resistance of the combination of resistors in Fig 4.16?

Example

$$\frac{1}{R_t} = \frac{1}{R_1} + \frac{1}{R_2}$$

$$\frac{1}{R_t} = \frac{1}{8\,\Omega} + \frac{1}{4\,\Omega}$$

$$\frac{1}{R_t} = \frac{1}{8\,\Omega} + \frac{2}{8\,\Omega} = \frac{3}{8\,\Omega}$$

$$R_t = \frac{8\,\Omega}{3} = 2.67\,\Omega$$

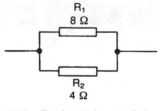

4.16   Resistors in parallel.

Notice that in a parallel circuit the total resistance is *less* than the smaller of the separate resistances. This is because the provision of an extra path must make it easier for the current to flow.

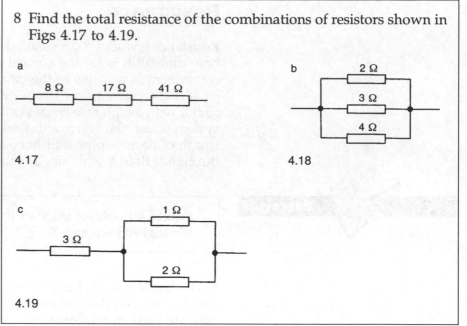

8 Find the total resistance of the combinations of resistors shown in Figs 4.17 to 4.19.

a

8 Ω   17 Ω   41 Ω

4.17

b

2 Ω
3 Ω
4 Ω

4.18

c

1 Ω
3 Ω
2 Ω

4.19

Ammeters

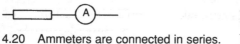

4.20   Ammeters are connected in series.

Ammeters measure electric current. The current must pass through them if they are to be able to measure it. Therefore ammeters must be connected in series with the circuit, see Fig 4.20. They must have a very low resistance so that they do not affect the current flowing.

Voltmeters

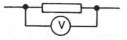
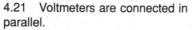

4.21   Voltmeters are connected in parallel.

Voltmeters measure potential difference between two points in the circuit. This is the energy difference which makes the current flow. Voltmeters must therefore be connected between the two points, see Fig 4.21. They must have a high resistance so that they do not allow a significant current to flow through them or they could affect the very thing we are trying to measure.

9 In Fig 4.22, where would you place a voltmeter to measure the potential difference across bulb A and an ammeter to measure the current through bulb B?

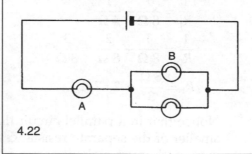

4.22

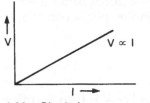

4.23 Ohm's Law.

4.24 Circuit to verify Ohm's Law.

The equation can be rearranged as $V = RI$. You can remember this with the phrase 'the **V**icar is a **R**eligious **I**nstructor'.

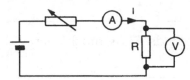

Exercise

Table 4.1 Current through, and potential difference across, a length of wire

Potential difference, V/ volts	Current, I/ amps	V/I
1	0.1	
2	0.2	
3	0.3	
4	0.4	
5	0.5	

Ohm's Law

In the 1820s, Georg Ohm investigated the electrical properties of metallic materials. He found that the current through any particular piece of metal (which we shall call a resistor) was always proportional to the potential difference across it, provided the temperature remained constant, see Figs 4.23 and 4.24.

Expressed mathematically,

$$I \propto V$$

where V is the potential difference across a resistor
  I is the current through the resistor

An alternative way of expressing the same thing is that, for a particular resistor, V/I is always a constant number. We call this constant R, the resistance of this resistor. In general,

$$R = \frac{V}{I} \quad \text{where } R \text{ is the resistance in ohms } (\Omega)$$

This equation can be used to calculate the resistance of any device.

A resistor has a resistance of 1 Ω if a current of 1 A flows through it when there is a potential difference of 1 V across it.

10 Table 4.1 gives values of current through and voltage across a length of wire, obtained using a circuit such as that in Fig 4.24.

   a For each pair of readings, work out V/I. Is it constant?
   b What is the resistance of the piece of wire in Ω?

11 What is the resistance of a bulb if the current through it is 2 A and the potential difference across it is 4 V?

12 What is the current flowing through a 5 Ω resistor if the potential difference across it is 20 V?

13 Two bulbs are connected in series as shown in Fig 4.25.

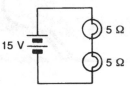

4.25

   a What is the total resistance of the two bulbs?
   b Now calculate the current flowing through the circuit.

14 Three resistors are connected in parallel as shown in Fig 4.26.

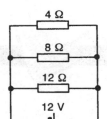

4.26

   a What is the total resistance of the resistors?
   b Now calculate the current taken from the 12 V supply.

15 A bulb has a resistance of 5 ohms in Fig 4.27. Calculate the value of the series resistance to limit the current to 0.2 amps from the 10 V supply.

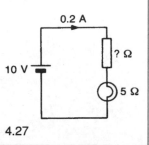

4.27

Power

Power is the rate of transforming energy from one form to another (see Chapter 2). Power is usually measured in joules per second, or watts (symbol W).

$$\text{power (watts)} = \frac{\text{energy (joules)}}{\text{time (seconds)}}$$

The 60 W bulb by which you may be reading this book is transforming 60 J of electrical energy into 60 J of heat and light energy every second.

Exercise

16 A 40 W bulb is switched on for 60 seconds. How much energy does it transform?

Electrical power

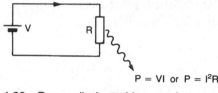

P = VI or P = I²R

4.28   Power dissipated by a resistor.

Whenever an electric current flows through a part of a circuit, some of the electrical energy is transformed into heat, see Fig 4.28. The rate of transformation of energy depends on the current flowing through the wire and the potential difference across it.

If there is a current of 2 A, two coulombs pass through the resistor each second. If there is a potential difference of 10 V, each coulomb gives up 10 J of energy as it passes through. So each second, $2 \times 10 \text{ J} = 20 \text{ J}$ is converted from electrical energy to heat. In general,

power = potential difference × current

$$P = VI$$

Most electrical domestic equipment is marked only with its power rating, so how do you calculate its current consumption to allow you to choose the correct fuse?

Example

An electric kettle has a power rating of 2000 W and operates from the 240 V mains. Which of the following fuses would you use: 1, 2, 3, 5, 7, 10, 13 A?

$$P = VI \quad \text{or} \quad I = \frac{P}{V} = \frac{2000 \text{ W}}{240 \text{ V}} = 8.3 \text{ A}$$

You must use a fuse a bit larger than this – a 10 amp fuse.

Exercise

17 What is the power of a 12 V bulb which has a current of 1 A flowing through it?

18 A car headlamp bulb has a power rating of 60 W. It runs from a 12 V battery. What is the current flowing through it? Given the range of fuses in the previous example, what size fuse would you use?

Calculating power developed in resistances

There is an important variant of $P = VI$.

$$P = VI \tag{1}$$

$$V = RI \qquad \text{this is Ohm's Law} \tag{2}$$

Substitute (2) into (1)

$$P = I^2R$$

This tells us that the power developed in a resistance is proportional to the square of the current. It has many important implications – see the box below.

The National Grid

The National Grid, see Fig 4.29, is the system which distributes electrical energy from power stations to homes, schools, factories and so on. It operates by using transformers (see Chapter 5) to step up the voltage to about 300 kV (300 000 V) and then step it down again to 240 V. Why?

The reason is to minimise the loss of power caused by heat generated in the power lines. Imagine we have to supply 10 kW (10 000 W) of power (enough to run ten electric bar heaters) through power lines of resistance 1 Ω.

We know that $P = VI$

$$P = 10\ 000 \text{ W}$$

so, $V \times I = 10\ 000 \text{ W}$

Case 1   We could choose to supply this power at 100 000 V. Substituting into the equation above,

$$100\ 000 \text{ V} \times I = 10\ 000 \text{ W}$$

$$I = 0.1 \text{ A}$$

The power loss (as heat) is given by $P = I^2R$ so the rate of heat loss will be 0.1 A × 0.1 A × 1 Ω = 0.01 W

That is, 0.01/10 000 of the power being supplied (0.0001%) is wasted heating up the power lines.

Case 2   We could choose to supply this power at 200 V, in which case the current, I, would be 50 A. Check that this is correct by a calculation like the one above.

The rate of heat loss is given by $P = I^2R$ so the rate of heat loss will be 50 A × 50 A × 1 Ω = 2500 W

That is, 2500/10 000 of the power being supplied (25%) is wasted heating up the power lines.

The choice between these two alternatives is not difficult!

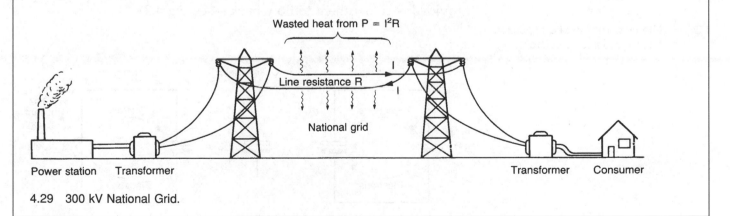

4.29   300 kV National Grid.

Electrical energy

We have seen that the power, P, generated by an electric current is given by:

$$P = VI$$

This is the energy transformed per second. If the current flows for a time t seconds, the total energy transformed, W, will be given by:

$$W = VIt$$

Exercise

19 A 3000 watt kettle is switched on for 2 minutes. How much energy has it transformed?

The capacitor

The capacitor stores electrical energy and in this way is similar to a rechargeable battery. The advantage of a capacitor is that it can both charge up with energy and then discharge the energy in a much shorter time than a battery. The disadvantage is that for a given physical size it holds much less energy.

An electronic flash on a camera takes a short time between switching on and the ready indicator appearing. The flash lamp needs a large amount of electrical energy in a few microseconds The battery supplies the electrical energy slowly to the capacitor. The capacitor then delivers this energy very quickly to the bulb. Compare the time it takes the ready light to come on with the length of time of the flash.

How a capacitor works

Anything which can gain or lose free electrons is a capacitor. Your own body acts as a capacitor every time you receive a static electric shock as you step out of a car. When you touch the car door to close it, the electrons flow back suddenly as a painful electric current.

The capacitor is constructed to enhance this effect. At its simplest it consists of two plates made of aluminium foil separated by a thin film of insulating material such as polythene. The foil and separating plastic are rolled up to take up as small a volume as possible and connections are made to each plate – see Fig 4.30.

If the plates of the capacitor are connected across a potential difference, charge will be removed form one plate and deposited onto the other. If the source of the potential difference is now disconnected, the charges will stay where they are until a path is provided to allow them to flow back – see Fig 4.31.

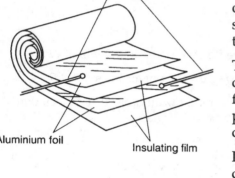

(a)

4.30 a   The construction of a capacitor.
b   The circuit symbol for a capacitor.

(b)

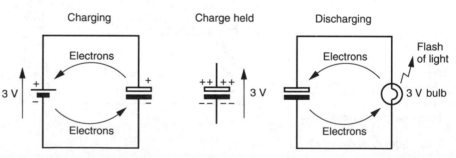

4.31   Charge and discharge of a capacitor.

The unit of capacitance – the farad

The charge-storing ability of a capacitor is called its capacitance and is measured in farads (F), named after Michael Faraday. For a given voltage pushing a charge onto a capacitor, the bigger the capacitance, the bigger the charge that the capacitor will hold.

One farad is a very large unit. A 1 farad capacitor, charged up to 240 V (mains potential), would store an energy of 30 000 joules and would need to be about the size of a small car. Compare this with a car battery which is capable of storing over 50 times the energy, but is about the size of a shoe box! A capacitor this size could be used to supply the energy to drive a pulsed laser capable of punching a hole in thin metal sheet. To obtain the power needed to do this, the energy must be delivered to the laser tube in much less than a microsecond – far more quickly than a battery could do it.

Most capacitors are much smaller than 1 F. We normally measure their capacitances in microfarads (μF).

1 microfarad (1 μF) = 1/1 000 000 of a farad.

The boxes below show some applications of capacitors.

The smoothing capacitor in a power supply

The ability of a capacitor to store and release electrical energy quickly is used in the design of power supplies.

In a typical power supply shown in Fig 4.32, the transformer (see Chapter 5) converts the mains potential difference of 240 V to 12 V for safe use in the classroom. The diode is an electronic component that allows current to flow in one direction only; we say that it **rectifies** the

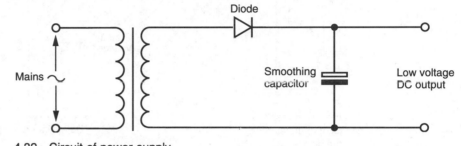

4.32   Circuit of power supply.

output. Fig 4.33a shows the output of the transformer and Fig 4.33b shows the output from the diode. It consists of a series of pulses of current occurring at the mains frequency of 50 Hz. If this supply were used to operate a radio it would result in a loud buzz being heard.

To avoid this, a large capacitor is connected across the output of the diode. Now when the output potential difference rises, not only does it supply the load with current, but it also charges up the capacitor. When the output of the diode falls and can no longer supply the load with current, the capacitor discharges through the load to supply the current instead. The output of the power supply is much smoother, as shown in Fig 4.33c.

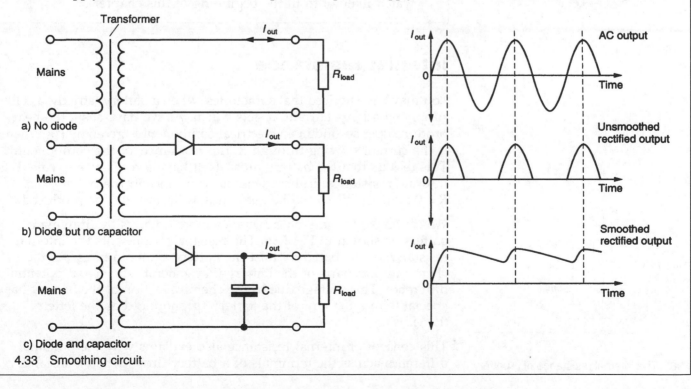

4.33   Smoothing circuit.

The capacitor in a timing circuit

If we connect a resistor in series with a capacitor as in Fig 4.34, it will slow down the rate at which the capacitor charges and discharges. The shape of the graph of the potential difference across the capacitor against time as it discharges is called an exponential – Fig 4.35. This is exactly the same shape as a radioactive decay curve – see Chapter 1.

The bigger the capacitance of the capacitor and the bigger the resistance, the longer the capacitor will take to discharge.

We can use this to design a circuit to delay the switching off of a light bulb so that you can turn off the light and still have time to get out of the room before it goes out. We use electronics to sense when the potential difference across the capacitor has fallen to a set fraction of its original value and switch the bulb off after this delay time.

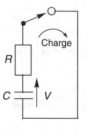

V_0 is the p.d. across the capacitor at the start of the discharge.

4.34   A capacitor discharging.

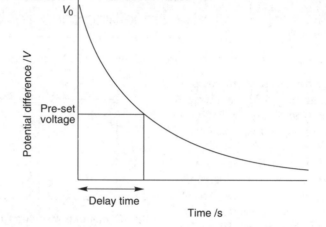

4.35   The discharge of a capacitor and its use in a time delay circuit.

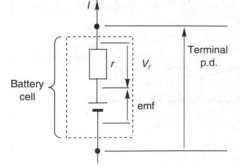

Exercise

20 Try to explain the operation of the capacitor in terms of the water analogy from the beginning of this chapter.

Internal resistance

You may have noticed that sometimes, when a battery (strictly, a cell) is supplying a large current, it gets warm. As we have seen, the heat produced per second in an electrical component is given by I^2R where I is the current flowing through R, the resistance, of the component. This tells us that the battery must itself have a resistance – called its **internal resistance**. If there were no resistance in the battery, (i.e. $R = 0 \ \Omega$) then I^2R would be zero and no heat would be produced.

We can make the internal resistance more obvious by drawing a battery as shown in Fig 4.36. The resistor r, represents the internal resistance of the battery whilst the battery symbol represents the chemicals and parts of the battery that generate the actual potential difference. This voltage due to the chemical action of the battery has a special term – the emf of the battery (pronounced as the letters 'E. M. F.').

This concept of internal resistance also explains why the potential difference across the terminals of a battery drops when a sizeable

4.36   The internal resistance of a battery.

current is taken from it. Ohm's law tells us that whenever a current, I, flows through a resistor r, there is a voltage drop V, across the resistor given by $V = Ir$. This voltage drop will reduce the emf to give a lower potential difference across the battery terminals.

However, if no current is taken from the battery, then there will be no voltage drop across the internal resistance. The terminal potential difference measured with no load on the battery is the value of the emf.

Example

A A battery has an emf of 1.5 V. If the internal resistance, r, is 2 Ω and the current taken from the battery is 0.2 A, we can calculate what the terminal potential difference will be.

$$\text{voltage drop across the internal resistance } r, \; V_r = I \times r$$

$$= 0.2 \text{ A} \times 2 \,\Omega = 0.4 \text{ V}$$

Therefore,

$$\text{terminal potential difference} = \text{emf} - V_r = 1.5 \text{ V} - 0.4 \text{ V} = 1.1 \text{ V}$$

B The terminal potential difference of a battery is measured as 2.2 V when no current is taken, but drops to 1.9 V when a current of 0.15 A is taken.

What is:

a the battery's emf?
b its internal resistance?
c the terminal potential difference when the load current is 0.25 A?

a when zero current flows there will be no voltage drop across r, so the terminal potential difference will equal the emf, i.e. emf = 2.2 V.
b voltage drop across r, $V_r =$ emf $-$ pd $= 2.2 - 1.9 = 0.3$ V
now, $r = V_r/I = 0.3 \text{ V}/0.15 \text{ A} = 2 \,\Omega$, so the internal resistance is 2 Ω.
c $V_r = I \times r = 0.25 \text{ A} \times 2 \,\Omega = 0.5$ V

Now, terminal potential difference $=$ emf $- V_r = 2.2 - 0.5 = 1.7$ V

Exercise

21 A car battery has a terminal potential difference of 15.5 V on no load. When a current of 20 A is taken, its terminal potential difference falls to 12.5 V.

a Draw a symbolised battery with internal resistance and label the emf, r, V_r, terminal potential difference and I.
Hint: it is often useful to sketch a diagram in electrical problems.
b Calculate the emf and internal resistance.
c What would the terminal potential difference become with a load of 30 A?

Chapter 5

Electromagnetism

- Do you understand the following terms: **direct current, alternating current**? Write a sentence or two (no more) to explain what you understand by each term, then check in the glossary.

Using electromagnetism

Did you know all the following devices (and many more) operate by electromagnetism?

- electric motors
- microphones
- loudspeakers
- electric bells and buzzers
- disc drives
- video recorders

The key to the operation of electromagnetic devices is the fact that a magnetic field is produced when an electric current flows.

Exercise

1 Write down at least three important facts about how magnets behave.

2 Draw the shape of the magnetic field around a bar magnet.

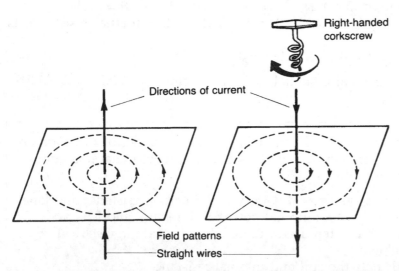

5.1   Magnetic field due to a straight wire and the corkscrew rule.

The magnetic effect of an electric current

The term 'field' describes how magnetic force reaches out through space. So magnets can attract and repel without touching. Magnetic fields are drawn as lines – the closer the lines, the stronger the field. These lines have arrows drawn on them which indicate the direction in which the North pole of a small magnet would point when placed in the field. Thus the field lines are shown going from north to south.

If a current flows along a straight wire, a circular magnetic field is produced, as shown in Fig 5.1. The direction of the field can be found by the 'corkscrew rule', as shown.

Exercise

3 Draw the field produced by the current flowing in Fig 5.2. Show its direction.

Current flow

5.2

Permanent magnets

Many people believe that permanent magnetism and electromagnetism are quite different. In fact they are due to exactly the same thing – the movement of charge. At the atomic level, negatively charged electrons 'spin' as they 'orbit' the nucleus. This spin makes each electron into a tiny electromagnet and if enough spins line up, the magnetism becomes strong enough to be noticed. Iron in particular shows this strongly, but other elements are magnetic to a lesser extent.

The magnetism of planets such as the Earth must also be due to the movement of charge, and it is thought that this may be due to the flow of ionised particles in currents in the molten interior of the Earth caused by its rotation.

Concentrating magnetic fields

Compared with a straight wire, a single turn of wire increases the magnetic field, as shown in Fig 5.3.

Circular 'turn'

Field line

Current direction

Wire

5.3   Magnetic field due to a single turn of wire.

Exercise

4 Use the corkscrew rule to check that the direction of the current in the turn of wire in Fig 5.3 has been given correctly.

The pole of a magnet that points to the geographical North of the Earth is called the north pole of that magnet. It is attracted to the south pole of other magnets. So the geographical North pole of the Earth is really the south pole of the Earth's magnetic field!

A solenoid (a long coil of wire, as shown in Fig 5.4) increases the field further still, as all the individual turns contribute to the overall field strength.

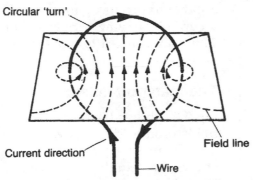

Solenoid   Field line

Current direction   Wire

5.4   Magnetic field due to a solenoid.

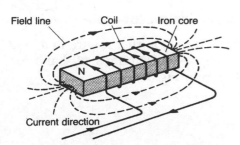

Field line   Coil   Iron core

N

Current direction

5.5   Electromagnet with an iron core.

Placing an iron core in the solenoid (Fig 5.5) increases the magnetic field still more, to make an even stronger magnet. This is because magnetic materials such as iron enhance magnetic fields.

The strongest magnets have their poles placed close together as in the electromagnet with an iron 'C' core (so called from its shape) shown in Fig 5.6. This is because the field has to pass through only a small distance of air.

The iron cores in Figs 5.5 and 5.6 become magnets while the current is flowing. The north pole is marked on Fig 5.5.

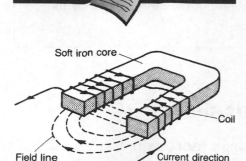

Soft iron core
Field line   Current direction
Coil

5.6   Electromagnet with an iron 'C' core.

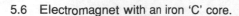

Exercise

5 Use the direction of the field lines to find which pole is north in Fig 5.6.

6 Give an application of electromagnets. Why are they more useful than permanent magnets?

The electric motor effect

In the electric motor, electrical energy is converted into kinetic (moving) energy. We know that one magnetic field interacts with another to produce a force (unlike poles attract and like poles repel). So a current-carrying wire has a force exerted on it by a magnetic field. This may cause it to move, as shown in Fig 5.7.

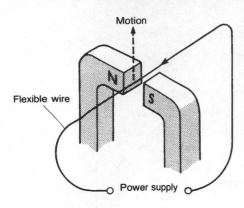

Motion
N   S
Flexible wire
Power supply

5.7   Current-carrying wire in a strong magnetic field.

Although it is the wire that we see moving, it is really the electrons inside the wire that have the force exerted on them.

The 'catapult' effect

Fig 5.8a shows the separate fields produced by the wire and the magnet. Fig 5.8b shows the resulting combined field. Note, here, how the field is concentrated on one side of the wire and weakened on the other. The result is that the wire appears to be in a 'catapult' which propels it at right angles to the magnet's field.

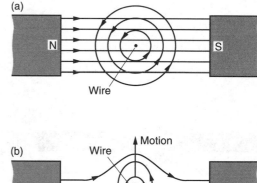

(a)
N   S
Wire

(b)   Wire   Motion
N   S

5.8   The catapult effect.

7 Mark on a copy of Fig 5.8b where the field is strongest and where it is weakest. Does the wire move from strong field to weak or from weak to strong?

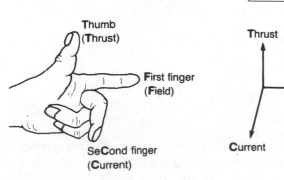

Thumb (Thrust)
First finger (Field)
SeCond finger (Current)

5.9   Fleming's left-hand (or motor) rule.

Thrust
Field
Current

Fleming's left-hand (or motor) rule

We can work out the direction that a wire in a magnetic field will move by Fleming's left-hand (or motor) rule, as shown in Fig 5.9.

Exercise

8 Work out the direction that the wires in Figs 5.10, a to c, would move.

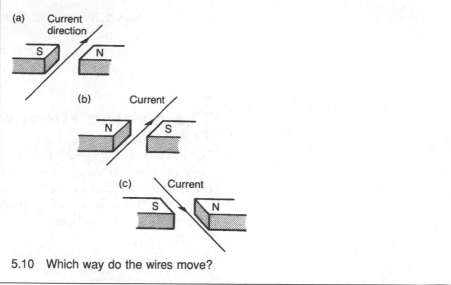

(a) Current direction

S   N

(b) Current

N   S

(c) Current

S   N

5.10   Which way do the wires move?

Direct current (DC) electric motor

If a wire can be moved by a magnetic field, it is a simple engineering problem to harness this movement usefully. Fig 5.11 shows a simple electric motor. The current flowing through the coil in the magnetic field creates a force on each side of the coil in the directions shown. The directions of these forces can be predicted using Fleming's left-hand rule. Check that you get the same directions as those shown by the arrows in Fig 5.11. As these forces are in opposite directions, they tend to make the coil rotate as shown. The electric current flows from the external circuit into the coil via carbon brushes which rest gently on the commutator. The commutator rotates with the coil so that the current always flows in the same direction around it.

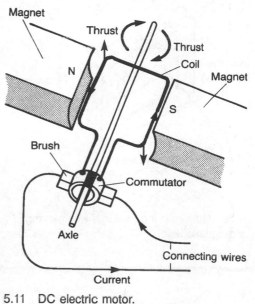

5.11   DC electric motor.

Direct current (DC) meter

The DC meter works on the same principle as the electric motor except that the coil turns against a spring and there is no need for a commutator. A simplified diagram of such a meter is shown in Fig 5.12. When a current flows through the coil, the coil twists in just the same way as it does in a motor. However, as it twists, it tightens up the coiled spring until the twisting force due to the current equals the opposing force due to the spring. So the bigger the current, the bigger the deflection of the meter. This is the basis of both ammeters and voltmeters.

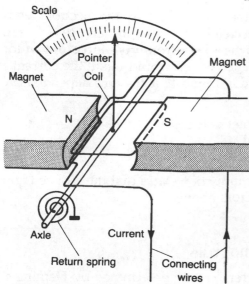

5.12   DC meter.

9 Suggest three ways of increasing the force which makes the DC electric motor work.

10 a Explain why the DC meter needs no commutator.
   b How could we make the DC meter more sensitive – that is get a bigger movement from the same current?

The electric effect of magnetism

We have seen how electricity creates magnetism. Now we will look at how magnetism can create electricity. This is known as **electromagnetic induction** and was discovered by Michael Faraday in 1831. It is the basis of all electrical generators. These convert kinetic energy into electrical energy.

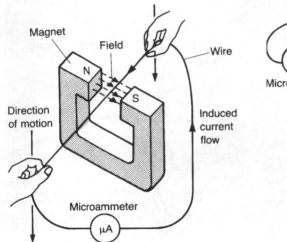

5.13 Current is induced in a wire moving in a magnetic field.

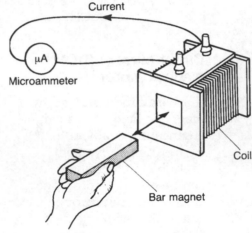

5.14 Current is induced in a coil by a changing magnetic field.

Electromagnetic induction

If a wire is moved through a strong magnetic field, as shown in Fig 5.13, the electrons are pushed to one side and flow along the wire as current. This induced current flows only whilst the wire is in motion.

A current is also induced if the magnet moves and the wire is still, see Fig 5.14. The important point is that only relative movement is needed.

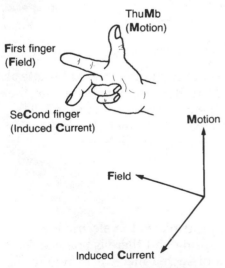

5.15 Fleming's right-hand (dynamo) rule.

If you have difficulty recalling which hand to use for which of Fleming's rules, remember that *motors* drive on the *left*.

Faraday's law of electromagnetic induction

If no circuit is connected across the coil in Fig 5.14, the electrons will build up at the end of the wire to create a potential difference across it. This potential difference is known as an **electromotive force**, or emf for short. This is the potential difference which would make the current flow if there were a circuit. Faraday found that the emf depended on three things:

- the relative speeds of the magnet and coil
- the number of turns of the coil
- the strength of the magnetic field

Faraday's law of electromagnetic induction states that the induced emf is proportional to each of the factors above.

Fleming's right-hand (dynamo) rule

The direction of the induced current can be determined by Fleming's right-hand (dynamo) rule, as shown in Fig 5.15.

Exercise

11 Work out the direction of the induced current in Figs 5.16 a and b.

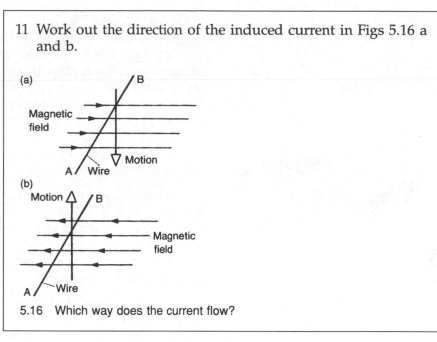

5.16 Which way does the current flow?

Direct current (DC) generator (dynamo)

Currents induced by wires moving in magnetic fields are the basis of electric generators, from bicycle dynamos to those used by the electricity supply industry.

If we consider the system for the DC electric motor (see Fig 5.11), but instead of supplying current, we supply drive to the axle, we can see that an emf will be induced and thus current will flow.

Exercise

12 Fill in the gaps in the following passage:

The DC generator converts_____energy into_____energy and the DC motor turns_____energy into_____energy.

You can convince yourself that motors can work as generators as follows. Connect a milli-ammeter across the terminals of a small DC motor, such as is found in some toys, and spin the axle. You will see a small current registered.

Alternating current (AC) generator

This is of even greater importance than the DC generator since mains electricity is AC so that it can be transformed up and down efficiently. See Chapter 4, The National Grid.

The only basic difference from the DC generator is that slip rings are used instead of a commutator, see Fig 5.17. As the coil rotates, the windings move alternately up through the magnetic field and then down again. This means that the induced current flows first in one direction and then in the other. The output current changes direction (or alternates) at the frequency of the rotational speed of the generator, which is 50 times per second (50 Hz) in the case of British mains supplies.

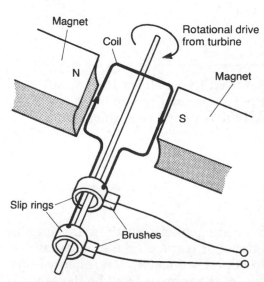

5.17 AC generator.

Transformers

Transformers are devices that can 'transform' a low potential difference up to a high potential difference and vice versa. They work only with AC supplies and are immensely important in the efficient transmission of electrical energy in the National Grid (see Chapter 4), where they transform the potential difference up for transmission, and then down again for use. Transformers are also used to produce low, and therefore safe, potential differences for such as electric model trains, cassette players and radios.

The construction and symbolic representation of a transformer are shown in Figs 5.18 a and b. Its operation is another example of electromagnetic induction. An alternating current (AC) is applied to the **primary coil** producing an alternating magnetic field in the iron core. This alternating magnetic field cuts the **secondary coil**, thus inducing an emf across it.

The following relationship applies to transformers:

$$\frac{V_s}{V_p} = \frac{N_s}{N_p}$$

where

V_p = potential difference applied across the primary coil
V_s = potential difference developed across the secondary coil
N_p = number of turns in the primary coil
N_s = number of turns in the secondary coil

This means that if we want to step up our potential difference, we must have more turns on the secondary coil than on the primary. It is the *ratio* of the number of turns on the secondary coil to the number of turns on the primary which determines by how much the transformer steps potential difference up or down. This is sometimes called the turns ratio.

(a)
Two iron 'C' cores clamped together
Secondary coil
I_s
V_s
Primary coil
I_p
Secondary connecting wires (N_s turns)
Primary connecting wires (N_p turns)
V_p

(b)
I_p
I_s
Alternating supply
V_p
N_p
N_s
V_s
Load
Primary coil
Secondary coil

5.18   a The physical construction of a transformer
  b Symbolic representation of a transformer.

Example

A transformer has a primary coil with 2000 turns and a secondary coil with 100 turns. A potential difference of 240 V is applied across the primary. What will be the output potential difference of the secondary?

$$\frac{V_s}{V_p} = \frac{N_s}{N_p} \quad \text{so} \quad V_s = \frac{N_s \times V_p}{N_p} = \frac{100 \times 240 \text{ V}}{2000} = 12 \text{ V}$$

The output potential difference is 12 V

Exercise

13 What turns ratio would you need to transform 10 kV (the output potential difference of a power station) up to 300 kV (the potential difference at which the National Grid transmits electrical energy)?

Transforming the current

At first sight it looks as though we are getting something for nothing from a step up transformer. However, if we step *up* the potential difference, we step *down* the current proportionately. If no energy is lost in a transformer, the power input (to the primary) will be the same as the power output (from the secondary).

Since electrical power, $P = VI$ (see Chapter 4)

$$V_p \times I_p = V_s \times I_s$$

where I_p = current flowing in the primary coil
I_s = current flowing in the secondary coil

Example

A transformer has a primary coil of 2000 turns and a secondary coil of 100 turns. This, as we have seen in the above example, will step down a primary potential difference of 240 V to 12 V. If the current flowing in the primary coil is 0.1 A, what current will flow in the secondary?

If no energy is lost,

$$V_p \times I_p = V_s \times I_s$$
$$240 \text{ V} \times 0.1 \text{ A} = 12 \text{ V} \times I_s$$
$$I_s = 2 \text{ A}$$

The transformer equation can be extended to

$$\frac{V_s}{V_p} = \frac{N_s}{N_p} = \frac{I_p}{I_s}$$

A current of 2 A will flow in the secondary coil.

The step down transformer offers a useful way of providing large currents for arc welding, industrial electromagnets and other high-current devices.

Exercise

14 A transformer transforms 240 V mains to 3 V for an arc welder.

a If the primary coil has 800 turns, how many turns will there be on the secondary?
b If the current in the welder is 250 A, what would be the primary current taken from the mains if no energy is lost?

Transformer efficiency

Transformers are very efficient devices.

Example

A A transformer has a potential difference of 400 V applied to its primary with a secondary potential difference of 1500 V. The secondary current supplied to the load is 2 amps. The current flowing in the primary is measured to be 8.5 amps. What is the efficiency of the transformer?

$$\text{Efficiency} = \frac{\text{power out}}{\text{power in}} \times 100\% = \frac{V_s \times I_s}{V_p \times I_p} \times 100\%$$

$$= \frac{1500 \text{ V} \times 2 \text{ A}}{400 \text{ V} \times 8.5 \text{ A}} \times 100\% = 88\%$$

B What would be the primary current in the above example if the efficiency was 60%?

Use the equation: $\text{efficiency} = \dfrac{\text{power out}}{\text{power in}} \times 100\%$

Rearrange this to give: $\text{power in} = \dfrac{\text{power out}}{\text{efficiency}} \times 100\%$

Substitute: $\text{power in} = V_p \times I_p$ and $\text{power out} = V_s \times I_s$

$$V_p \times I_p = \frac{V_s \times I_s}{\text{efficiency}} \times 100\%$$

$$I_p = \frac{V_s \times I_s \times 100\%}{V_p \times \text{efficiency}}$$

Now put the values in:

$$I_\mathrm{p} = \frac{1500\ \mathrm{V} \times 2\ \mathrm{A} \times 100\%}{400\ \mathrm{V} \times 60\%} = 12.5\ \mathrm{A}$$

Note that the % signs can be cancelled in exactly the same way as units.

Exercise

15 What would be the primary current in the above example if the efficiency were   a 100%   b 80%?

Causes of transformer energy losses

There are four basic sources of inefficiency in transformers. These are worth looking at, both because transformers are so important in the electricity supply system and because the same inefficiencies also occur in other electromagnetic mechanisms such as motors, electromagnets and relays. They result in energy being lost as heat. You may have noticed this yourself in, for example, mains adaptors for personal stereos, which get quite hot in operation. These transformers are designed to be compact at the expense of efficiency.

1 Heat losses due to resistance of the windings

In Chapter 4 we saw that any electrical component with resistance produces heat at a rate given by $P = I^2R$. The windings of the transformer have resistance and so will cause these 'I^2R' losses. Thicker wires would reduce the losses, but then there might not be enough room on the transformer to wind the number of turns needed.

2 Eddy currents

The transformer core, being made of iron, will itself conduct electricity. So a current – called an eddy current – will also be induced within the core in the same way as the current is induced in the secondary coil. If the core has low electrical resistance, a very large current will flow in it which will generate a lot of heat.

To keep eddy currents to a minimum, the resistance of the core is raised by constructing the core out of thin slices of 'laminates' of iron with non-conducting coatings.

3 Magnetic field losses

The electrical energy from the primary coil is transferred to the secondary coil via the magnetic field in the core. If the core is not big enough or efficient enough magnetically, all the energy will not be transferred to the electrical output.

4 Hysteresis losses

Magnetism is produced by aligning the spins of electrons in iron atoms (see p.61). As the transformer operates with alternating current, this means that the magnetic field in the core must be alternating and that the alignment of the electron spins must also be alternating. It takes energy to align the electron spins and this energy appears as heat in the transformer core.

Some of these losses are shown in Fig 5.19.

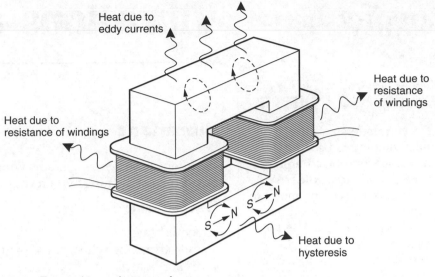

5.19   Energy losses in a transformer.

Chapter 6

Vibrations and waves

Example

Vibrations

We often come across systems which vibrate or oscillate (the two words mean the same thing) when they are started off with a push.

Here are some examples:

- pendulums
- taut strings or wires, such as guitar strings
- diving boards
- tall buildings
- swings
- columns of air, such as those inside woodwind instruments

A swinging pendulum completes twelve oscillations in three seconds. Calculate

a the time period
b the frequency of the oscillation.

a One oscillation is the movement of the pendulum starting from any point in its swing, through a complete swing and back to the point. The time period is the time it takes to do this.
   Thus time period, $T = $ total time taken/number of oscillations
   $= 12$ s$/3 = 4$ seconds

Frequency is measured in vibrations per second, called **hertz**, Hz.

b The frequency of an oscillation is the number of vibrations that occur in one second.

   Each vibration takes 4 seconds, so the frequency is
   $1/(4$ s$) = 0.25$ vibrations per second or 0.25 Hz.

Exercise

1 A swinging light completes eight oscillations in two seconds. Calculate

   a the time period,
   b the frequency of the oscillation.

In some cases vibrations are very useful to us, as in musical instruments and pendulum clocks. Others can be dangerous. For example, the Tacoma Narrows Bridge in Washington State, USA, was destroyed in 1940, by out-of-control vibrations. It is important to understand what is going on in this kind of motion.

A very simple example to think about is a child's swing, see Fig 6.1. This is an example of a pendulum. If you look closely at this motion you will see that the speed of the swing is constantly changing. At each end of the actual oscillation, the swing itself is stationary. Its speed builds up (it accelerates) as it approaches the centre of its oscillation, where it is going fastest. One full oscillation of the swing is from A to D and back to A.

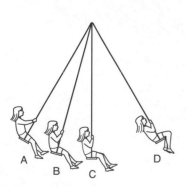

6.1 A child's swing.

An object hung on a spring is another simple example, see Fig 6.2. If the object is pulled down so that the spring stretches and is then released, it will oscillate in an up and down motion. Again the speed will vary between zero at the extremes, W and Z, and a maximum at the central position, Y. The central position for the spring system will be the normal unstretched position.

Exercise

2 a Using the letters shown in Figs 6.1 and 6.2, identify, for both the swing and spring systems, the positions of
i maximum speed   ii zero speed
iii a speed lower than maximum.

b Write down the amplitude of each of the systems.

Simple harmonic motion

Some oscillations, though not all, have a very important characteristic – they keep the same time period even though the size or amplitude of the oscillation may change. This is true in the case of both of the above examples. The pendulum clock is a further example. When the amplitude of the oscillation gets less, the maximum speed is reduced. This means that the time taken to cover the smaller distance is the same as the time to cover the original larger distance. The kinds of systems which have this particular characteristic are usually called **simple harmonic oscillators**.

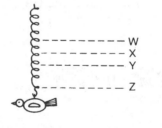

6.2

Forced vibrations and resonance

Oscillations tend to lose energy as they move and work against friction. The swing, for example, is working against the air and against its bearings. As an oscillation loses energy its amplitude will decrease. We can, however, prevent this by giving it a push at just the right time. The timing of the push is very important and we must also select the correct position and direction when we push a swing. If we were to choose a different timing, the response of the swing to our repeated pushes would be very poor. We can tell our timing is right if the swing starts to build up its amplitude. This happens only when the frequency of the pushing force exactly matches the **natural frequency** of the oscillation. We call this situation **resonance**.

Exercise

3 Where, when and in what direction, would you push a swing to build up its amplitude of vibration?

Resonance

There are many situations where resonance can be useful. For example, a diver from the high board builds up amplitude by jumping up and down at exactly the natural frequency of the board. Another, less obvious, example is tuning in to electrical oscillations with a radio receiver. But sometimes resonance can be dangerous. Examples include the effect of earthquakes on buildings, and regular ruts in the road which cause car bodies to oscillate. In the latter case steps must be taken to prevent the build up of amplitude. Car suspensions are designed so that oscillations will die out quite quickly: we say the oscillations are heavily **damped**. In the former case, it is important to take the natural oscillation frequency of tall buildings into account in their design.

Waves

Waves and vibrations or oscillations are often confused. This is because they are usually found together. A vibration is necessary to start a wave, and it is this vibration which is passed on to the parts of the material or **medium** that the wave travels through.

6.3   A transverse wave passing along a slinky spring.

In Fig 6.3, imagine someone at the left side of the spring, who makes one complete up and down movement or oscillation of the left-hand link in the spring. As this link moves, it pulls the next link up with it. In this way the movement made by the first link is repeated all the way along the spring. Each link, however, lags slightly behind in the oscillation compared to the link before it. This results in the spring taking up a shape like that shown in Fig 6.3. It is this shape that we call a wave. It travels along the spring from left to right carrying with it the energy of the vibration.

There are two movements at right angles to each other in this example – the oscillation (up and down) and the moving wave (along the spring). We call this type of wave a **transverse** wave.

It is possible to send a different type of wave through the spring. The link at the left can be made to vibrate to and fro along the length of the spring. As before this will cause successive links to follow its movement, but lagging slightly behind until the vibration finally arrives at the other end. In this case the vibration and the travelling wave are both along the same line and the wave is called a **longitudinal** wave, see Fig 6.4.

6.4   A longitudinal wave passing along a slinky spring.

Waves, in general, fall into either of these two categories: transverse or longitudinal.

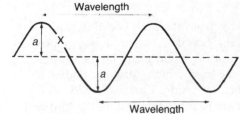

Exercise

4 Suggest into which category each of these waves fits.

   a Ripples (waves) travelling across a still pond causing a toy boat to move up and down.
   b A loudspeaker causing the air to oscillate and pass a sound wave.
   c A wave produced by flicking a skipping rope.

Wave measurements

Fig 6.5 shows the side view of a transverse water wave. The wave is actually travelling, so the diagram shows its position at an instant in time (as though we had taken a snapshot of it).

Wavelength

There are two crests and two troughs shown in Fig 6.5. This means that two full oscillations have occurred. The **wavelength** is the distance

Wavelength

a X

a

Wavelength

a is the amplitude

6.5   Transverse waves.

from any point on one wave to the same point on the next wave. For simplicity it is usually measured from crest to crest or from trough to trough. It is given the symbol λ, the Greek letter lambda.

> 5 If point X on Fig 6.5 is taken as the starting point for the wavelength measurement, mark the point Y where the measurement would end.

Some of the measurements made on the waves are the same as those for oscillations.

Frequency

As the waves pass along, the number of complete up and down vibrations which pass any particular point in one second is called the **frequency**. This must be the same as the number of vibrations which are made in one second at the source of the wave. We measure frequency in waves per second or cycles per second. One cycle per second is given the name hertz (Hz).

Amplitude

This is the furthest distance that the parts of the medium move from their undisturbed position. It is set by the amplitude of the oscillating source of the wave.

The wave formula

Waves often spread out in a circle from the source (think of ripples formed by dropping a stone in a pond). Sometimes, we think about a part of the wave which is moving in one particular direction, so we tend to talk about its **velocity** (see Chapter 3) rather than its speed. This is simply the distance that the wave travels in one second in a particular direction.

The velocity, v, is measured in metres per second (m/s).
The wavelength, λ, is measured in metres.
The frequency, f, is measured in waves per second or hertz (Hz).

These three values can be combined into the relationship:

$$v = f\lambda$$

A Let us look at where this relationship comes from. Imagine you are watching the waves pass you. For each complete vibration, the wave itself moves on by one whole wavelength, say 0.2 metres. In one second a certain number of waves moves past, say 6 waves per second. So every second, the wave must move forward by 6 × 0.2 metres. This means that the velocity of the wave is 6 × 0.2 metres per second, that is, 1.2 metres per second.

In this example, 6 waves per second is the frequency, f, and 0.2 metres is the wavelength, λ. Multiplying these together gives us the velocity of the wave, v.

B A small branch, driven by the wind, is oscillating up and down with a frequency of 10 Hz. The branch is dipping into a shallow pond

and the wavelength of the ripples travelling across the pond is
1.7 cm. Work out the velocity of the ripples.

$$v = f\lambda = 10\ \text{Hz} \times 1.7\ \text{cm} = 17\ \text{cm/s}$$

The relationship $v = f\lambda$ is true for all waves. Practise using it to answer
the following questions.

6 a A wave has a frequency of 2 Hz and a wavelength of 10 cm.
     Work out the velocity of the wave.
   b Waves travel along a spring at 150 cm/s. The end of the spring
      is oscillated at 20 vibrations per second. Calculate the
      wavelength of the waves.
   c Radio waves of wavelength 1515 metres (Radio 4) have a
      frequency of 198 000 Hz. Calculate the velocity of these waves.
   d Assuming that all radio waves travel at the same speed, work
      out the frequency of 275 metre wavelength waves.

Properties of waves

There are certain properties that all waves have. These are **reflection**, **refraction**, **diffraction**, and **interference**. In
fact the scientist Thomas Young suggested, in the early 19th century, that light was a wave rather than a stream
of particles when he demonstrated that it was possible both to diffract light and to cause it to interfere. Scientists
had been discussing the nature of light for some time.

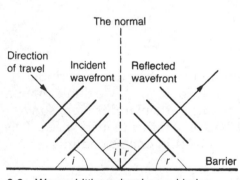

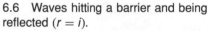

6.6 Waves hitting a barrier and being
reflected ($r = i$).

Reflection

You are probably quite familiar with reflection. Check with the
glossary that you understand the terms: **angle of incidence**, **angle of
reflection**, **the normal** and the relationship between the angle of
incidence, i, and the angle of reflection, r. These are shown in Fig 6.6.

Refraction

Refraction or bending occurs when a wave moves out of one substance
and into another. It occurs because the wave travels at different speeds
in different materials.

Fig 6.7 shows water waves in a ripple tank moving from deep to
shallow water. The waves travel
more slowly in the shallow region
as there is more drag on them. This
means that the **wavefronts** are
closer together in the shallow area,
so the wavelength has become
smaller. As the right-hand side of
the wave spends more time in the
shallow region, it falls behind the
left-hand side. This means that the
wave is bent as it moves into the
shallow region. We say the wave
has been **refracted**.

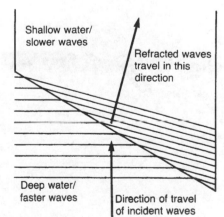

6.7 Refraction of water waves.

Exercise

7 a How (if at all) will the frequency be affected by this slowing down of the wave?
  b Does this fit with the wave relationship $v = f\lambda$?

8 Fig 6.8 shows light being refracted as it moves from air into glass.

  a Draw in the wavefronts on a copy of the diagram.
  b Does the light wave travel more slowly in the air or in the glass?
    (Use Figs 6.7 and 6.8 to help you.)

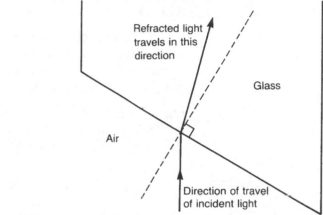

6.8   Refraction of light waves.

9 Fig 6.9 shows water waves travelling in both deep and shallow regions of a ripple tank.

  a Identify the shallow region on each photograph.
  b In Fig 6.9a, the wave direction shown by the arrow does not change but in Fig 6.9b it does. Suggest why this might be so.

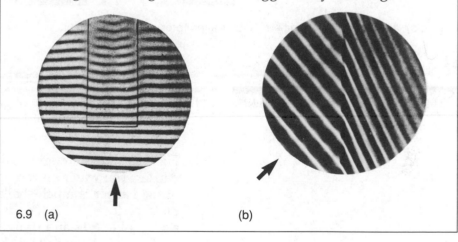

6.9   (a)   (b)

Diffraction

Diffraction is the spreading out of waves as they pass through narrow gaps. Figure 6.10a shows water waves being diffracted as they pass through a gap in a harbour wall. However, we cannot see around corners, so does this mean that light waves are not diffracted?

Figs 6.10b and c, which show diffraction in a ripple tank, can help us explain the difference. In each case the straight waves pass through a gap in the barrier. In Fig 6.10b, where the wavelength of the wave is

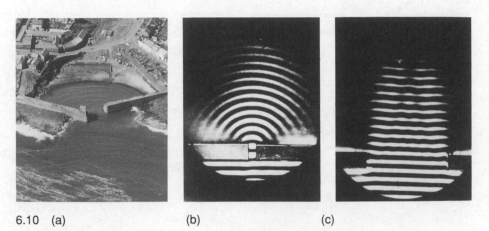

6.10   (a)   (b)   (c)

about the same size as the gap, there is significant spreading out or diffraction. This is the situation with the water waves and the harbour mouth – the waves are of about the same wavelength as the size of the gap in the harbour wall.

Fig 6.10c is more like the situation that occurs with light. The wavelength is very small compared with the size of the gap, and the diffraction effect is much less obvious.

It is possible, however, to find a gap of the correct size so that diffraction of light does occur. Fig 6.11 shows the pattern obtained on a screen when light is passed through a very narrow vertical slit (0.01 mm wide).

The middle band of the light strip is much wider than the original slit and there are further bands of light to the left and right. This shows that the light wave has spread out as it passed through the slit.

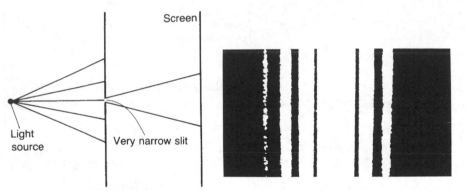

6.11   (a) Aerial view of experiment.   (b) Pattern produced at the screen.

Exercise

10 On the basis of the size of gap that produces diffraction, make a very rough estimate of the wavelength of
    a water waves in the sea   b light waves.

11 Fig 6.12 shows straight waves in a ripple tank approaching a barrier. The water on the right-hand side of the barrier is much shallower than that on the left.
    a Copy Fig 6.12 and draw in the wave, after they have passed through the gap.
    b Add arrows to the diagram to show the directions of the waves both before and after they go through the barrier.

6.12

Interference

This occurs when two (or more) waves meet. Each wave will affect the material or medium through which it is travelling. In water, for example, each wave may cause the water at a particular point to rise up (form a crest). The total effect will be that the water will rise by a

6.13   Interference in a ripple tank.

greater amount, in fact by the sum of the heights of the individual crests. Similarly, where two troughs of the waves meet, there will be a deeper trough, equal to the sum of the two troughs. Where the crest of one wave meets the trough of the other, and they are both of the same height, they will add to produce calm water.

However, in the water we have many waves and the movements caused by each of the waves add together. We call this the **principle of superposition** and we say that the waves have interfered.

Fig 6.13 shows interference of waves in a ripple tank. S_1 and S_2 are sources of circular waves. You can see the alternate regions of still and disturbed water.

To help us to explain the appearance of the water we need to construct a diagram like the one in Fig 6.14.

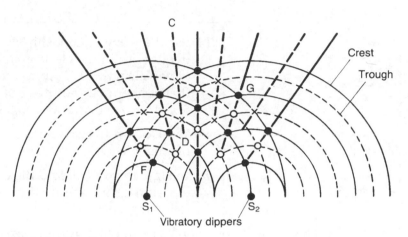

6.14   Interference

This lets us see what effect each wave would have at particular points. For example, points such as F in the diagram show where a crest from S_1 meets a crest from S_2. This will result in a high crest being produced. As another example, the line that joins C to D will have a crest meeting a trough at every point. This corresponds to a line of calm water. The overall pattern produced is called an **interference pattern** and its appearance is related to the wavelength of the waves which produce it.

Exercise

12 a Use a ruler to measure the wavelength of the waves in Fig 6.14.
  b What would you expect to see at position G?
  c Use a ruler to measure the length of a line from S_1 to position G. How many wavelengths is it?
  d Use a ruler to measure the length of a line from S_2 to position G. How many wavelengths is it?

13 Fig 6.15 shows waves spreading out from two sources, S_1 and S_2. $\frown$ = crest

  a What part of the wave (crest or trough) is at A and which source is it from?
  b In the region where the waves overlap, explain how the waves will combine at positions B and C.

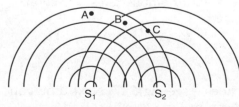

6.15

Electromagnetic waves

There are many different types of waves – for example water, sound, radio, gamma, and light. They all have the properties of reflection, refraction, diffraction and interference.

Some of these waves can be organised into a special group called the **electromagnetic spectrum**. They are all transverse waves which travel at a speed of three hundred million metres per second (often called the speed of light). They are able to travel through a vacuum. The reason for the name electromagnetic is that the waves all consist of oscillating electric and magnetic fields. The word spectrum indicates that the group covers a very wide range of wavelengths. The wavelengths in fact vary from as small as a million millionth of a metre for gamma rays to several kilometres for radio waves.

---

14 use the wave relationship $v = f\lambda$ to work out the range of frequencies in the electromagnetic spectrum from gamma rays of wavelength 10^{-12} m to radio waves of wavelength 10^5 m. (Remember that the speed of all of these waves is the same, 3×10^8 m/s, that is, 300 000 000 m/s.)

15 Write down five properties which are common to all electromagnetic waves.

16 In Fig 6.16 you will find the different waves which belong to the electromagnetic spectrum. Study this and then try to answer the following questions.

　a Write down a list of at least five waves which make up the electromagnetic spectrum. Place them in order of increasing wavelength.

　b State from your own reading, which waves cause a suntan. Calculate their frequency, using the typical wavelength.

　c How many times longer is the wavelength of microwaves than the typical wavelength of X-rays? From your own reading, which of them is more penetrating?

Sound waves

Sound differs from water and electromagnetic waves in that it is a longitudinal wave (see p. 72) and that we sometimes use different terminology such as **pitch** for frequency and **loudness** for amplitude. **Tone** refers to the mixture of frequencies which give a sound its characteristic identity.

Sound is, nevertheless, a wave and the use of wave calculations is very important in understanding how our hearing works, the design of musical instruments, loudspeakers and sonar systems, amongst others. Just like all the other types of wave, sound demonstrates reflection, refraction, diffraction and interference.

Reflection of sound

Reflection of sound gives rise to echoes – see Fig 6.17. Next time you get the chance, time the delay between making a loud sound and

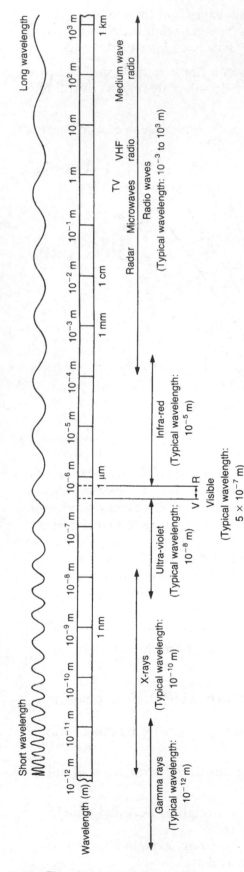

6.16   The electromagnetic spectrum.

hearing its echo. Estimate the distance the sound has travelled (remembering that the sound has to make a there-and-back trip) and calculate the speed of sound using speed = distance/time. You should come up with an answer around 340 m/s. Alternatively, use the known speed to calculate the distance the sound has travelled.

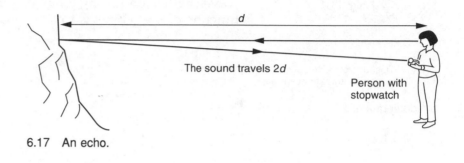

6.17 An echo.

Refraction of sound

People who live some miles from a railway may not normally be able to hear the trains. But on a still summer's night they may hear the trains very clearly indeed. This is because a temperature inversion in the atmosphere has occurred. Warm air is trapped underneath colder air owing to the ground remaining warm after the sunset. Sound travels more slowly in cold air than in warm air and the sound waves are refracted back down to the ground so that they can be heard. See Fig 6.18. Under more normal conditions when the warm air is on top of the cold, the sound bends in the opposite direction and goes up into the sky. This refraction of sound happens in exactly the same way that water waves bend when slowed down in shallow water, or light bends when passing between glass and air.

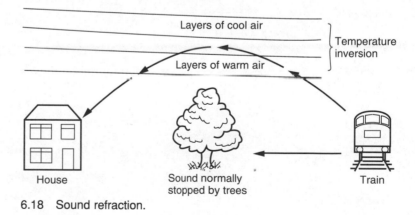

6.18 Sound refraction.

Diffraction of sound

You can hear somebody talking in another room without having to stand opposite the door. This is because sound waves have approximately the same wavelength as the size of the door-opening and they are diffracted as they pass through it. This happens in an identical manner to the picture of water waves diffracted from a slit, in Fig 6.10. Similarly, when you talk, the sound waves spread out from your mouth right around to the back of your head.

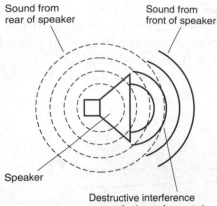

Sound from
rear of speaker

Sound from
front of speaker

Speaker

Destructive interference
occurs for lower frequencies

6.19   Sound interference.

Interference of sound

If you listen to music from a loudspeaker fitted in a cabinet and then listen to the same speaker out of the cabinet, there is a clear difference in sound. When removed, the speaker sounds 'tinny' (lacking in the lower frequency sounds). This is because the longer wavelength (lower frequency) sound waves produced at the back of the speaker cone travel around the side and destructively interfere with the same wavelength sound being emitted from the front of the speaker. The function of the cabinet is to stop this happening.

Chapter 7

More nuclear physics

The inverse square law

In Chapter 1 we saw how Rutherford worked out that the atom has a positively charged nucleus by considering the deflection of alpha particles. To do this he used the inverse square law.

The repulsive force between two positive charges gets smaller as they get further apart. If the distance is doubled the force is reduced by a factor of 4. If the distance is increased by a factor of 3, the force is reduced by a factor of 9. This kind of relationship is called an **inverse square law**. You will come across it in a number of situations.

Inverse square law

The force between two electric charges, $F_{electric}$, is described by Coulomb's law. It looks quite daunting but, become familiar with it and use it as a recipe to get answers, and it's not so bad.

$$F_{electric} = \frac{9 \times 10^9 Qq}{r^2}$$

where $Q =$ the first charge, $q =$ the second charge, $r =$ the separation between the charges

---

Example

If two protons are separated by a distance of 10^{-10} m, what force pushes them apart? The charge on a proton is 1.6×10^{-19} C

$$F = \frac{9 \times 10^9 \, Qq}{r^2}$$
$$= \frac{9 \times 10^9 \times 1.6 \times 10^{-19} \times 1.6 \times 10^{-19}}{10^{-10} \times 10^{-10}}$$
$$= \frac{9 \times 10^9 \times 2.6 \times 10^{-38}}{10^{-20}}$$
$$= 2.3 \times 10^{-8} \text{ N}$$

Alpha particles and energy

For their size, alpha particles are really quite energetic and in a head-on encounter with a gold nucleus they can get very close before they are brought to a stop and then repelled away by the repulsion of the positively charged gold nucleus. An alpha particle with an energy of 1.1×10^{-12} J can approach the nucleus to within 3.2×10^{-14} m. At this distance the repulsive force acting on the alpha particle is about 36 N. This is a lot of force for a particle with a mass of only

Example

6×10^{-27} kg.

What is the force on the alpha particle when it is 6.4×10^{-14} m from the gold nucleus?

At 3.2×10^{-14} m the force is 36 N

We can use the inverse square law here: double the distance, reduce the force 4 times.

6.4×10^{-14} m is twice 3.2×10^{-14} m

Twice the distance means one-quarter the force so the force is $36 \times 1/4 = 9$ N

Exercise

1 What force acts on the alpha particle when it is 12.8×10^{-14} m from the gold nucleus?

---

100 g of alpha particles

10^{-12} J is a very small amount of energy. So it may seem strange that alpha particles are referred to as very energetic. The problem is that we have no feel for these small numbers. We do, however, know what 100 grams is like (roughly the mass of an apple). How much energy would 100 g of alphas have? Rounding our figures to the nearest power of ten to make the calculation simpler,

100 g $= 0.1$ kg

mass of 1 alpha particle $= 10^{-26}$ kg

number of alphas to make 0.1 kg $= 0.1/10^{-26} = 10^{25}$

energy of 100 g of alpha particles $=$ number of alphas $\times$ energy of one alpha

$$= 10^{25} \times 10^{-12}$$
$$= 10^{13} \text{ J}$$

This is the energy you would need to lift 200 000 elephants to the top of Snowdon!

Ionisation

When alpha particles pass through matter they interact with the electrons around the nucleus. As the alphas passes by, it exerts attractive forces on the negative electrons and can pull some of them away from the atom. In other words it can **ionise** atoms. The energy required to remove an outer electron in this way is called the **ionisation energy**.

Example

Typically an alpha particle could have 6 MeV of energy. As it passes through the air it loses, on average, 30 eV each time it ionises an atom. How many ion pairs can it create?

energy of the alpha particle $= 6 \times 10^6$ eV

energy to create ion pair $= 30$ eV

To find how many ion pairs can be created, we divide the total energy available by the energy needed to create one ion.

$$\text{number of ion pairs produced} = \frac{6 \times 10^6}{30} = 2 \times 10^5$$

2 Alpha particles are emitted with energies in the range of about 4 MeV to 10 MeV. What is the energy in joules of

a the least energetic alpha particle
b the most energetic alpha particle?

Energy from the nucleus

In Chapter 1, we saw that we can get energy from atomic nuclei in two ways, by breaking down large nuclei (fission) and by joining together smaller ones (fusion). Here we will look at where this energy comes from.

Mass defect

The word 'nucleon' refers to the particles found in the nucleus – protons and neutrons.

The protons and neutrons in a nucleus are held together by a force called the **strong nuclear force**. This is what stops the protons flying apart. If you were to try to 'unpick' a nucleus you would have to do a lot of work against this force; to pull the nucleons apart you must give them energy. This means that in the nucleus the nucleons are at a lower energy level than when they are free. This energy deficit is called **binding energy**. In essence, any nucleus that exists lost energy when it formed from separate protons and neutrons. You can compare the situation to rocks falling into a valley and coming to rest on the valley floor. (Try to describe the energy change which would take place.) The deeper the valley the more energy lost in the fall and the lower the energy level of the rocks.

Very accurate measurements of nuclear masses shows that nuclei have less mass than the total mass of the protons and neutrons that make them up. This lost mass is called the **mass defect**. To understand its significance we need to remember that mass and energy are equivalent. Einstein's famous equation summarises the conversion from one to the other:

$$E = mc^2$$

Where m is the mass and c the speed of light, 3×10^8 m/s.

So the mass defect is matter turned into energy; the energy lost when the nucleus formed. The mass defect then is equivalent to the binding energy.

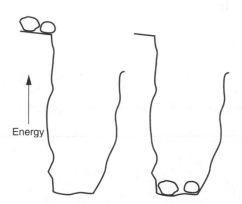

7.1   Rocks lose energy if they fall into a valley.

This is easier to understand by looking at an example. Let us take an alpha particle – the nucleus of a helium atom.

The helium nucleus has a mass of 4.002 u and consists of two protons and two neutrons. The mass of a proton is 1.007 u and the mass of a neutron 1.009 u.

mass of two protons and two neutrons $= (1.007 \times 2) + (1.009 \times 2)$

$= 4.032$ u

The mass defect is the difference between the expected mass and the actual mass

mass defect $= (4.032 - 4.002)$ u

$= 0.030$ u

The masses of atoms are measured in atomic mass units, symbol u. $1\ u = 1.661 \times 10^{-27}$ kg.

$1\ u = 1.661 \times 10^{-27}$ kg, so

$$0.030\ u = 0.030 \times 1.66 \times 10^{-27}\ \text{kg}$$
$$= 4.983 \times 10^{-29}\ \text{kg}$$

To find out how much energy this is we use Einstein's equation.

$$E = mc^2$$
$$= 4.983 \times 10^{-29}\ \text{kg} \times (3 \times 10^8\ \text{m/s})^2$$
$$= 4.485 \times 10^{-12}\ \text{J}$$

This is the binding energy of the helium nucleus.

Exercise

3 What is this energy in MeV?

4 What is the binding energy per nucleon?

5 Why would it be reasonable to quote this binding energy as a negative number?

As the size of nuclei increases, the total binding energy also increases. The link between the two is almost linear. The binding energy per nucleon, however, is not constant. The way in which binding energy per nucleon changes is shown in the graph of Fig 7.2 and this variation has some very important consequences. In medium sized nuclei (in the middle of the graph), nucleons are bound more strongly and occupy lower energy levels than in either small nuclei (to the left of the graph) or large nuclei (to the right). If we could make medium sized nuclei from small ones or large ones, we could get this energy out and use it. This is what happens in fission and fusion.

The binding energy is negative as it is a *loss* of energy.

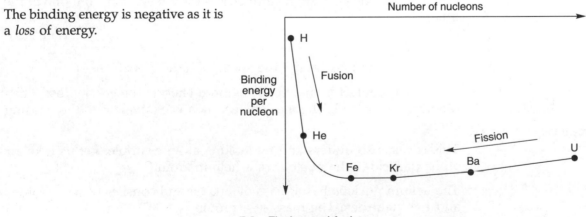

7.2   Fission and fusion.

Nuclear fission

In nuclear fission a large nucleus splits into two smaller nuclei and releases energy. This is what happens in nuclear reactors enabling vast amounts of energy to be generated. It is a real application of mass–energy equivalence.

The nucleus of uranium-235 can be broken up. If the nucleus absorbs an extra neutron it becomes unstable and splits producing new nuclei and *two* neutrons. These in turn split other uranium atoms. This is called a chain reaction – see Fig 7.3.

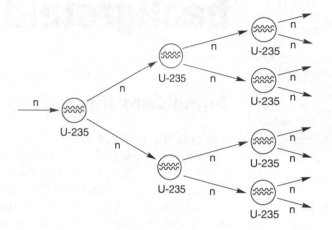

7.3 A chain reaction.

The nucleus can break up in a number of ways, one of which is shown below

$$^{235}_{92}U + {}^{1}_{0}n \rightarrow {}^{144}_{56}Ba + {}^{90}_{36}Kr + 2{}^{1}_{0}n$$

If you look at the graph of Fig 7.2 you can see that the nucleons in barium (Ba) and krypton (Kr) are at lower energy levels than when they are in the uranium (U) nucleus. Each nucleon gives up energy in this change and this appears as kinetic energy of the products which is transferred to the reactor core as heat energy.

Exercise

6 How many nuclei would there be in 1 kg of uranium-235? Hint: there are 6.02×10^{23} nuclei in 1 mole (235 g) of uranium-235.

7 Typically, when a uranium-235 nucleus splits it releases 200 MeV of energy.

a How many nuclei would be present in 500 g of U-235?
b What is the energy yield in MeV?
c What is this in joules?

Fusion

If you look at Fig 7.2 again you can see that if you started with two light nuclei and made them combine you would end up with a nucleus with lower energy nucleons. The graph, however, is much steeper at this end and so the energy released by each nucleon would be greater. So this looks like a better option for generating energy. The problem with this approach is that you must force together the positively charged nuclei. This is possible if the nuclei are hot enough and therefore move fast enough. This process happens in the Sun which is a vast fusion reactor. To copy this process on Earth we need to produce and control very high temperatures – a technically very difficult challenge.

Chapter 8

Mathematics background

STARTING POINTS

You will need a scientific calculator – one with the following
functions as well as the four basic
arithmetical functions:

- square and square root

- log and antilog (to base 10 and
  base e)

- exponential

- x^y

- brackets

- sin, cos and tan

Not all of these functions will be
needed for this chapter.

Significant figures

Imagine the price of identical juggling clubs in different shops is:
£15.98, £13.97, £14.92, £13.99, £21.11. Now if we are going to compare
prices to see which is the cheapest, we look first at the tens of pounds.
This allows us to eliminate the most expensive. We now look at the
pounds themselves. This allows us to eliminate the next two most
expensive. We repeat this process until we are comparing the pennies,
when we can work out the cheapest. This could not be successfully
done starting the other way around.

In this process we compared the **most significant figure** and worked
through to the **least significant figure**. The most significant figure in
any number is the one nearest the left-hand end of the number
(provided it is not zero).

For example, in the number 1236.358

the 1 thousand is the	most significant figure
the 2 hundreds is the	2nd significant figure
the 3 tens is the	3rd significant figure
the 6 units is	4th significant figure, and so on.

When approximating the value of a number, it is usually written to
include a specified number of significant figures. How many we use
depends on the situation. We might want to quote the length of the M1
to the nearest km, the size of a snapshot to the nearest mm, the
thickness of a sheet of paper to the nearest 1/100 mm.

For example, the number 1 291 573 is written as 1 290 000 to three
significant figures. All the unwanted figures are turned to 0 so the
number retains its value.

If when approximating to 3 sf (three significant figures) the 4th sf is a 5
or greater, then the 3rd sf is rounded up by one unit.

A Express 5387.043 to 3 sf.

Here the 7 is the 4th sf and the 8 is the 3rd sf. To express this number
to 3 sf we need to change the 3rd sf from its value of 8 to 9. So
5387.043 is 5390 to 3 sf. (Note: To 5 sf, this would become 5387.0.)

B Express 0.040 359 2 to 3 sf.

Here the 5 is the 4th sf and the 3 is the 3rd sf. So 0.040 359 2 = 0.0404
to 3 sf.

There are times when this process of rounding up can seem to reduce
the number from 3 sf to 1 sf, as the following example demonstrates.

Express 59 999.0 to 3 sf. Here the 4th sf is 9, so the 3rd sf must be
rounded up. The 3rd sf is a 9. If it is rounded up it becomes 10. This
affects the 2nd sf which must also be rounded up. The 2nd sf is a 9. If it

is rounded up, it too becomes a 10. This affects the most significant figure. This too is rounded up.

Result: 59 999.0 to 3 sf becomes 60 000.

This result is the same as for 59 999.0 to 1 sf. But, in fact, when the answer is 60 000 to 3 sf, the first two zeros following the 6 *are* significant.

> 1 Express the following to 3 sf.
>
>   a 1452.3   b 9 841 667   c 41.882   d 1.999   e 0.8992
>   f 0.002 009 9
>
> 2 Write the following to 2 sf.
>
>   a 200.3   b 80.6   c 4.902   d 0.0205   e 0.005 96   f 99.8

Powers of ten

The table below shows what happens as we multiply ten by ten an increasing number of times.

$$10 \times 10 = 100 = 10^2$$
$$10 \times 10 \times 10 = 1\ 000 = 10^3$$
$$10 \times 10 \times 10 \times 10 = 10\ 000 = 10^4$$
$$10 \times 10 \times 10 \times 10 \times 10 = 100\ 000 = 10^5$$
$$10 \times 10 \times 10 \times 10 \times 10 \times 10 = 1\ 000\ 000 = 10^6$$

So $10^7 = 10\ 000\ 000$. It also follows that $2 \times 10^4 = 20\ 000$. The superscripts following the 10s are the powers to which 10 has been raised. Any number can be written in this form.

> 3 Write out the values of the following:
>
>   a 3×10^5 b 22×10^2 c 6.3×10^7
>   d 0.4×10^3 e 1.43×10^6 f 81.89×10^2

Multiplying and dividing powers of ten

What happens if we multiply two powers of ten?

$$10^2 \times 10^3 = 100 \times 1000 = 100\ 000 = 10^5$$
So, $10^2 \times 10^3 = 10^{2+3} = 10^5$
$$10^3 \times 10^4 = 1000 \times 10\ 000 = 10\ 000\ 000 = 10^7$$
So, $10^3 \times 10^4 = 10^{3+4} = 10^7$

To multiply two numbers expressed as powers of ten together you have to add the powers of ten.

What happens if we divide powers of ten?

$$10^6 / 10^3 = 1\ 000\ 000 / 1000 = 1000 = 10^3$$
So $10^6 / 10^3 = 10^{6-3} = 10^3$

When dividing by powers of ten you have to subtract the powers of ten.

To multiply or divide two numbers such as 6.3×10^4 and 2.1×10^2, we can deal with each part of the number independently. So,

$$6.3 \times 10^4 \times 2.1 \times 10^2 = (6.3 \times 2.1) \times (10^4 \times 10^2) = 13.23 \times 10^6$$

and

$$6.3 \times 10^4 \div 2.1 \times 10^2 = (6.3 \div 2.1) \times (10^4 \div 10^2) = 3.0 \times 10^2$$

It is not quite so easy to see the meaning of powers that are less than 2.

$$10^3/10^2 = 1000/100 = 10$$

but, $10^3/10^2 = 10^{3-2} = 10^1$

So, 10^1 must be 10

$$10^2/10^2 = 100/100 = 1$$

but, $10^2/10^2 = 10^{2-2} = 10^0$

This means $10^0 = 1$. This is an extremely important result, In fact *any* number to the power $0 = 1$.

What about powers that are less than 0?

$$10^2/10^3 = 100/1000 = 1/10 = 0.1$$

but, $10^2/10^3 = 10^{2-3} = 10^{-1}$

So, $10^{-1} = 1/10 = 0.1$

This leads to $10^{-2} = 1/100 = 0.01$

$10^{-3} = 1/1000 = 0.001$

$10^{-4} = 1/10\,000 = 0.0001$ and so on.

Summing up:

- When 10 is raised to a power bigger than 1, this tells you the number of zeros to put after the first 1.
- When 10 is raised to a negative power (less than zero), the size of the number tells you which digit after the decimal point starts the number.

Exercise

4 Without using a calculator, work out the value of

a $10^3 \times 10^3$ b $5 \times 10^2 \times 0.02$ c $8.3 \times 10^4 \times 10^7$
d $10^2 \times 10^5 \times 10^7$ e $4 \times 10^4 \times 7 \times 10^5$

5 Without using a calculator, work out the value of

a $10^7 \div 10^3$ b $10^4 \div 10^3$ c $5042 \div 10^2$
d $4 \times 10^5 \div (2 \times 10^3)$ e $8 \times 10^4 \div (2 \times 10^4)$

6 Without using a calculator work out the following which involve subtracting negative numbers.

a $10^2 \div 10^{-2}$ b $3 \div 10^{-3}$ c $3 \times 10^4 \div 10^{-6}$
d $3 \times 10^{-3} \div (2 \times 10^{-4})$ e $0.22 \times 10^{-6} \div (0.88 \times 10^{-9})$

Use a calculator for questions 4 to 6, to see if your answer is the same.

Standard form

Standard form is a system where all numbers are expressed as a number between 1 and 10 multiplied by a power of ten. The idea behind this is to make very large and very small numbers easier to handle. By this system,

3129   becomes 3.129×10^3
and   0.009 723   becomes 9.723×10^{-3}

The system can also be used to help us approximate to a limited number of significant figures. For example,

7 813 845 782   becomes 7.81×10^9 to 3 sf
and   0.000 000 041 476 38   becomes 4.148×10^{-8} to 4 sf

Exercise

> 7 Write out the following numbers in full:
>
> a 3.98×10^4 b 5.773×10^7 c 1.002×10^{-3}
> d 8.224×10^{12} e 6.88×10^{-11} f 3.882×10^0
>
> 8 Write the following numbers in standard form to 3 sf:
>
> a 3 155 368 b 0.000 200 553 c 1.033
> d 0.000 000 053 3 e 88 545 447 822

Rearranging formulae and relationships

Whenever a mathematical formula or relationship is written down in a text book, you are always left with the impression that this is the way it should be written. However, you can rearrange it to suit your needs. You can even combine a number of them to produce a more suitable formula or relationship for yourself.

For example, we know that $V = IR$ (Ohm's Law). Suppose we know the values of V and R and wish to find I, that is, we want to make I, instead of V, the subject of the relationship.

R is multiplying I, so to cancel this effect we must divide both sides of the equation by R. Thus, $V/R = IR/R$.

We can now cancel the R values on the right side of the equation so, $V/R = I$. I is now the subject of the relationship.

When changing the subject of a mathematical formula or relationship, you need to strip off the other variables from around whatever you want to become the new subject. You need to undo or cancel any mathematical operation being done to it.

There are three pairs of mathematical operations which are in common use. Each one of the pair undoes or cancels what the other does. The three pairs are:

    ADD   .... SUBTRACT
    MULTIPLY   .... DIVIDE
    SQUARE   .... SQUARE-ROOT

Example

A Make R_1 the subject of $R_t = R_1 + R_2$.

To undo the effect of adding R_2, subtract R_2 from both sides of the equation.

$R_t - R_2 = R_1 + R_2 - R_2$
$R_t - R_2 = R_1$

B Make t the subject of $v = d/t$.

To undo the effect of dividing by t, multiply both sides by t.

$vt = dt/t$
$vt = d$

To undo multiplying by v, divide both sides by v.

$vt/v = d/v$
$t = d/v$

C Make v the subject of $v^2 = 2E/m$

To undo the effect of squaring v, take the square-root of both sides.

$$\sqrt{v^2} = \sqrt{(2E/m)}$$
$$\therefore v = \sqrt{(2E/m)}$$

Exercise

9 Make each variable in turn the subject of these relationships.
a $P = VI$ b $E = VIt$ c $a = (v - u)/t$
d $s = \dfrac{at^2}{2}$ e $E = \dfrac{mv^2}{2}$

Combining equations

It is possible to combine two or more equations into one equation. This is generally used to simplify problems. For example,

if $a = b + c$ and $a = de$
then we can say $de = b + c$

This is possible because both of the expressions on each side of the equals sign are equal to a, and so are equal to each other.

Now we have a new single equation which does not contain the variable a. We say we have **eliminated** a. One reason for doing this is if the value of a is difficult or inconvenient to measure. We can now rearrange the combined new equation, as needed. For example,

making c the subject $c = de - b$
or making e the subject $e = (b + c)/d$

When eliminating terms, you don't have to rearrange the equations you are starting with so they both have the same subject. This may be difficult and inconvenient. Instead, you can replace one variable with its equivalent value. For example, if $g = h^2$ and $j = kg + mg^2$ and we are trying to eliminate g, there is no need to rearrange the second equation. We can, instead, replace g by h^2 everywhere we find a g. So now,

$$j = kh^2 + m(h^2)^2 = kh^2 + mh^4$$

Exercise

10 Combine the following equations.

a $S = (v + u)/2$ and $S = d/t$

Eliminate S; make v the subject.

b $E = mgh$ and $E = mv^2/2$

Eliminate E; make h the subject.

c $p = mv$ and $E = mv^2/2$

i Eliminate m; make v the subject.

ii Eliminate v; make m the subject.

d $F = ma$ and $v = u + at$

Eliminate a; make u the subject.

e $F = ma$, $a = v^2/r$ and $v = r\omega$

Eliminate a and v; make r the subject.

Vectors

Vectors are used where there is a need to specify a direction as well as a size for a quantity. For instance it is often important to know the direction of a force as well as its strength. In other problems we may want to deal with both the direction and speed of a body.

A vector has both magnitude (size) and direction.

This is as opposed to a **scalar** which has magnitude only. Force and velocity are vectors, whilst temperature and energy are examples of scalars.

Finding the resultant force of two forces

When two forces act together they will add and produce the equivalent effect of one force known as the **resultant** force.

Fig 8.1a shows two tugboats towing a ship. One is more powerful than the other. We can use the rules for adding vectors to calculate the resultant force.

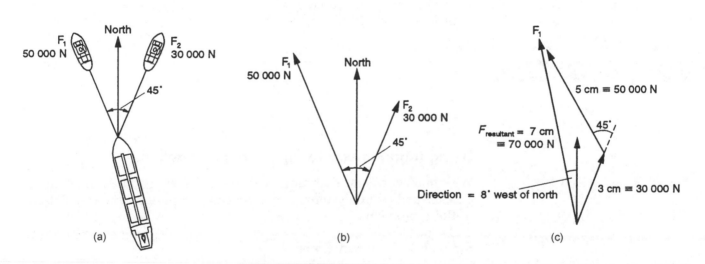

8.1   a Tugboats pulling a ship. b Space diagram. c Force diagram.

One way is by doing a scale drawing. Draw two vector arrows on paper in exactly the same directions that each tug is pulling as indicated in Fig 8.1b. Make the length of the vectors proportional to the magnitude of the force, for example use a scale of 1 cm = 10 000 N. This is called a **space diagram** because it represents the actual layout of the forces. Now draw a second diagram with the vectors head to tail but with the same length and direction, as in Fig 8.1c. Draw in the resultant from the beginning of the first arrow to the end of the second as shown. This is called a **force diagram**. The angle the resultant points in gives the direction of the overall force and the length gives its size. Measure the length of the resultant's arrow on your scale diagram and work out the size using the scaling factor.

Example

Two newtonmeters suspend a 1 kg mass (which has a weight of 10 N) at the angles shown in Fig 8.2a. What are the readings on the two newtonmeters?

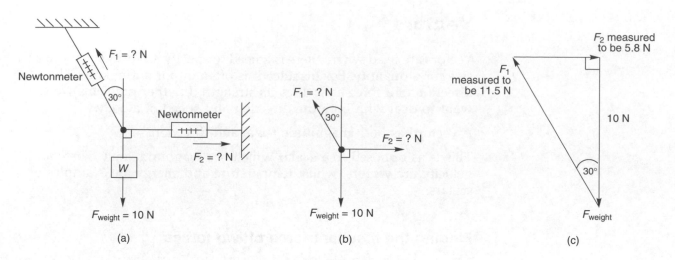

8.2   a Forces involved in suspending a weight. b Space diagram. c Force diagram.

1 Draw the space diagram – Fig 8.2b. This cannot be drawn to scale as we do not know the magnitudes of F_1 and F_2 yet.
2 Construct the force diagram to scale using the known angles of 30° and 90°, the 10 N length of the vector representing the weight of the 1 kg mass – Fig 8.2c. Measure the lengths of the unknown force vectors and you should get $F_1 = 11.5$ N and $F_2 = 5.8$ N. You could set up the system in the lab and verify that these two forces are correct.

11 Find the resultant force of 500 N northwards and 300 N eastwards by scale drawing.

Using trigonometry to solve vector problems

We can solve vector diagrams with scale drawings, but it is often quicker and certainly more accurate to use trigonometric calculations in these problems.

Sin, cos and tan functions

You have three trigonometric function buttons on your scientific calculator – sin, cos, and tan. You can use these buttons to make calculations concerning triangles and other geometric shapes.

Fig 8.3 shows the relationships between the trigonometric functions of one of the angles of a right-angled triangle and the ratio of two of the sides. These sides are called adjacent (adj.), opposite (opp.) and hypotenuse (hypot.).

$$\sin \theta = \frac{\text{opp.}}{\text{hypot.}} \qquad \cos \theta = \frac{\text{adj.}}{\text{hypot.}} \qquad \tan \theta = \frac{\text{opp.}}{\text{adj.}}$$

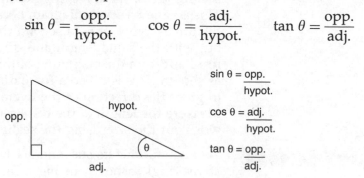

8.3   Trigonometric relationships of a right-angled triangle.

Make sure your scientific calculator is set to degrees – see your calculator instructions.

Example

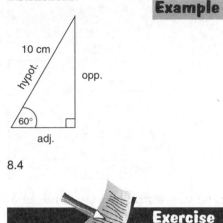

10 cm

hypot.

opp.

60°

adj.

8.4

Calculating the ratio of the sides of a right angle triangle from one of the angles

In a right-angled triangle with one angle of 60° and hypotenuse of 10 cm, what is the length of the opposite side?

sin 60° = opp./hypot., so put 60 into your calculator and press the sin button. You should get an answer of 0.8660 to four significant figures. This means that if the length of the hypotenuse is 10 cm, the length of the opposite side is 8.66 cm.

You might like to check this by drawing a scale diagram and measuring the ratio of the sides. Repeat the exercise for the other sides using the other functions. You should find that the adjacent side is 5 cm long.

Exercise

12 Use your calculator to find the following:

    a sin 30°

    b tan 15°

    c cos 68°

13 Work out the length of the side labelled x in the following triangles.

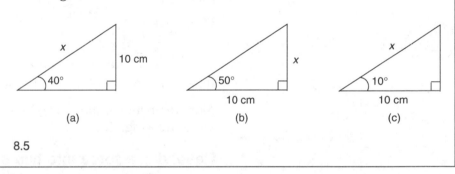

      (a)   (b)   (c)

8.5

Calculating the angle from the ratios of the sides of a right angle triangle

Example

In the right angled triangle in Fig 8.6 what is the angle a?

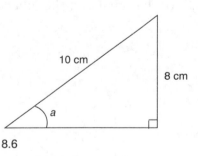

10 cm

8 cm

a

8.6

The ratio of opp./hypot. = sin a = 8/10. Look closely at your calculator keypad and you should see that your sin key changes into a sin⁻¹ key when you press the **inv** or **2ndF** key. This does the opposite to the sin key and calculates the angle from the ratio of the sides.

Do the calculation of 8/10 and then press the combination of keys to give you sin⁻¹ on your calculator. You should get an answer of 53.1°.

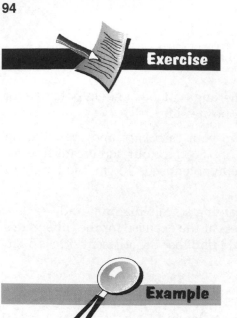

Exercise

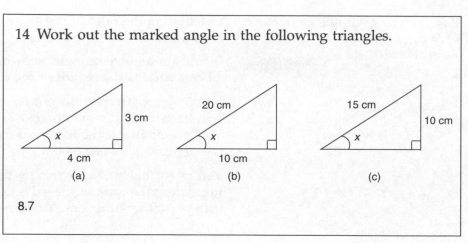

14 Work out the marked angle in the following triangles.

3 cm / 4 cm (a)

20 cm / 10 cm (b)

15 cm / 10 cm (c)

8.7

Example

Look back at the example above with the newtonmeters suspending a 10 N weight. Let us see how it can be solved without scale drawing.

1 Draw the space diagram as in Fig 8.2b.
2 Now draw the force diagram as in Fig 8.8 which in this case does not need to be to scale.

Finding F_1:

$$\cos 30° = \frac{\text{adj.}}{\text{hypot.}} = \frac{10\,\text{N}}{F_1}$$

therefore $F_1 = \dfrac{10\,\text{N}}{\cos 30°} = 11.5\,\text{N}$

Finding F_2:

$$\tan 30° = \frac{\text{opp.}}{\text{adj.}} = \frac{F_2}{10\,\text{N}}$$

therefore $F_2 = \tan 30° \times 10\,\text{N} = 5.8\,\text{N}$

Not surprisingly, these are the same answers as we obtained from the scale drawing.

Resolving a force into two components

It can often be helpful to break down one force into two which, together, have the same effect. These forces are called **components**.

Consider the situation in Fig 8.9a where a horse is pulling a barge along a canal with a force of 1000 N. The force exerted by the horse (F_{rope}) can be thought of as the resultant of two forces; one (F_1) pulling along the length of the canal and the other (F_2) pulling towards the bank. If we

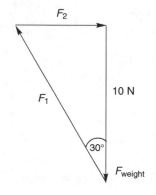

8.8

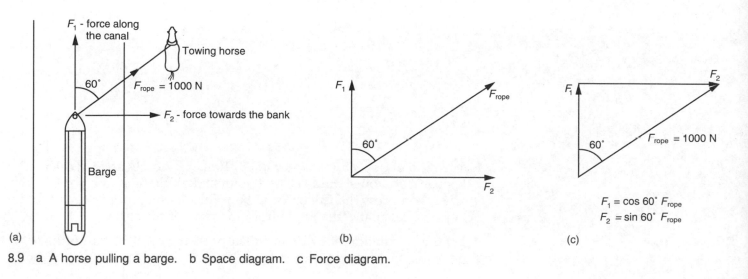

8.9 a A horse pulling a barge.   b Space diagram.   c Force diagram.

$F_1 = \cos 60°\, F_{rope}$
$F_2 = \sin 60°\, F_{rope}$

draw a scale diagram (Fig 8.9b) we can measure the forces F_1 and F_2 provided we know F_{rope} and the angle at which it acts.

Try to solve this problem by scale drawing; you should find that $F_1 = 500$ N and $F_2 = 866$ N.

Alternatively we can solve the problem by trigonometry (Fig 8.9c).

To find F_1:

$$\cos 60° = \frac{\text{adj.}}{\text{hypot.}} = \frac{F_1}{F_{\text{rope}}}$$

therefore $F_1 = \cos 60° \times F_{\text{rope}} = \cos 60° \times 1000 \text{ N} = 500 \text{ N}$

To find F_2:

$$\sin 60° = \frac{\text{opp.}}{\text{hypot.}} = \frac{F_2}{F_{\text{rope}}}$$

Therefore $F_2 = \sin 60° \times F_{\text{rope}} = \sin 60° \times 1000 \text{ N} = 866 \text{ N}$

Summary of using vectors

Finding resultant forces

1 Draw the space diagram showing the size, direction and point of action of each vector.
2 Draw the force diagram with the vectors moved to be head to tail.
3 Measure or calculate the size and direction of the resultant.

Resolving a force into components

1 Draw the force desired to be resolved as a vector.
2 Draw a right-angled triangle with this force as the hypotenuse.
3 Measure or calculate the other two sides of the triangle which are the two components.

Exercise

15 Look at Fig 8.2 again. If the angle of the newtonmeter measuring F_1 was at 45° from the vertical, what are the forces F_1 and F_2?

16 Use scale diagrams to find the tension (pulling force) in the strings holding up the picture frame in Fig 8.10 when the angle θ between the strings is   a 30°   b 45°   c 60°. The space and force diagrams are drawn for you.

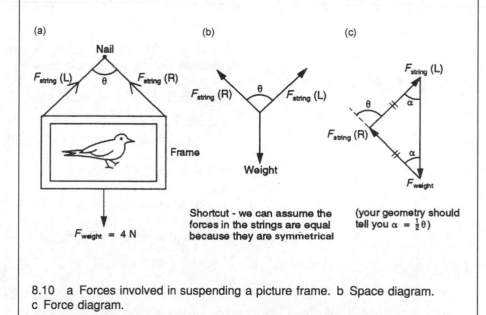

8.10   a Forces involved in suspending a picture frame. b Space diagram.
c Force diagram.

Exercise

17 A land yacht has a wind blowing in its sails to produce a force at 25° to the right of the direction it is steering in, with a magnitude of 1500 N. Resolve this force into the component in the direction of forward movement to find the magnitude of the propulsive force. Also resolve the component at right angles to the forward motion, to find the stress in the wheels and chassis.

Graphs

Graphs are often plotted to try to determine if there is any relationship between two or more variables. There are three basic outcomes of plotting a graph – a straight line, a curved line, and a scatter plot.

Straight line – see Fig 8.11. This tells us that the variables x and y are related by the equation $y = mx + c$.

m is the **gradient** of the line. The larger the value of m, the steeper the slope. If the sign of m is positive, the line slopes up from left to right, and if the sign of m is negative, the line slopes down from left to right.

If $c = 0$,   the line passes through the origin and $y = mx$. We say that x is proportional to y, often written $x \propto y$.

Curved line   A smooth curve tells us there is a relationship between x and y but not a directly proportional one.

Scatter plot   This type of plot, with points all over the place, that cannot be joined up to form straight lines or curves, tells us there is no obvious connection between variables x and y.

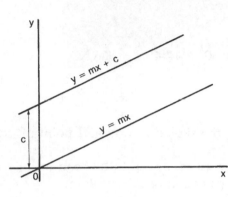

8.11   Straight line graphs.

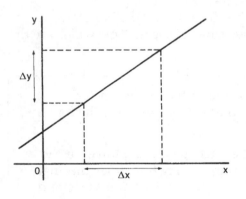

8.12   The gradient of a straight line.

Finding gradients

The gradient of a straight line

$$\text{gradient} = \frac{\text{the change in } y}{\text{the change in } x}$$
$$= \Delta y / \Delta x$$

For a straight line it does not matter how big Δy and Δx are; the gradient is always the same, see Fig 8.12.

The gradient of a curved line

Curved lines change their gradient all the time. We can find the gradient at any point by drawing the **tangent** to the curve at that point. We can then find the gradient of the tangent in the same way as for the straight line, see Fig 8.13.

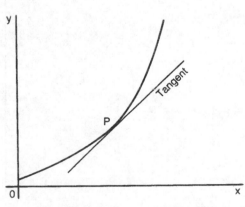

8.13   The gradient of a curve at a point P.

18 Work out what sort of relationship (if any) exists between the following variables.

a
X	1	2	3	4	5	6	7
Y	3	5	7	9	11	13	15

b
P	2	3	4	5	6	7	8
Q	1	2.25	4	6.25	9	12.25	16

c
H	1.8	1.9	2.0	2.1	2.2	2.3	2.4
W	84	71	78	86	82	66	80

19 Plot graphs and draw the best straight lines for the following. Then work out the gradients.

a
x	2.2	2.3	2.4	2.5	2.6	2.7	2.8
y	0.31	0.33	0.34	0.36	0.37	0.39	0.4

b
x	29	34	38	42	47	55	63
y	9.7	11.3	12.7	14	15.7	18.3	21

20 Plot a graph of x against y and estimate the gradient of the curve at points   a $x=2$ b $x=5$ and   c $x=7.4$

x	1	2	3.4	4.6	5.5	6.3	7.6	8.3	9.2
y	1	4	11.6	21.2	30.3	39.7	57.8	68.9	84.6

Glossary

Acceleration: A measure of how quickly velocity changes. (31, 36)

Activity: The number of nuclei of a radioactive substance which decay in a given time. (6)

Alpha radiation: Particles composed of two protons and two neutrons which are ejected from the nuclei of atoms. (6, 81)

Alternating current (AC): Electric current that regularly reverses the direction in which it flows. (65, 67)

Amp (ampere): The S.I. unit of electric current. (47)

Amplitude: The distance from the centre to the maximum position of an oscillation. (70, 72)

Angle of incidence: The angle that the ray which is incident on a surface makes with the normal. (74)

Angle of reflection: The angle that the ray which reflects off a surface makes with the normal. (74)

Atom: The smallest particle of any element. (2)

Background radiation: The radiation which is always present in the environment due to emissions from rocks, the atmosphere and cosmic rays, etc. (10)

Beta radiation: Fast-moving electrons which are ejected from the nuclei of atoms. (7)

Capacitor: A device that stores electrical energy. (56)

Conductor: A material that allows electrons to flow through it easily. (46)

Coulomb: The unit of charge (symbol C). One coulomb is 6.25×10^{18} electrons. (46)

Damped oscillations: Oscillations which lose energy as they vibrate. (71)

Diffracton: The spreading out of waves as they pass through gaps or around obstacles. (75, 79)

Direct current (DC): Electric current flowing in one direction only. (47, 57, 63, 65)

Displacement: A measure of how far an object is from a given point in a specified direction. (70)

Electric circuit: A combination of electrical components connected together to form a complete path for an electric current. (47)

Electric current: The flow of charge (electrons). (47)

Electromagnetic induction: The production of a current in a wire when the magnetic field across the wire changes. (64)

Electromagnetic waves: Waves which have electric and magnetic components. They all travel at the speed of light and are grouped into a family called the electromagnetic spectrum. (78)

Electromotive force (emf): A potential difference which drives a current around a circuit. (58)

Electron: A negatively charged particle found outside the nuclei of atoms. It has a mass of about 1/2000 of that of a hydrogen atom. (2, 4, 46, 49)

Electronvolt: A unit of energy. $1 \text{ eV} = 1.6 \times 10^{-19} \text{ J}$. (4)

Energy: The ability to do work (move the point of action of a force). (12–27, 83)

Equations of motion: A set of equations allowing calculations concerning motion. (37)

Exponential decay: This means that the amount of substance reduces by a constant factor in equal time intervals, for example reducing by half in the first two minutes, then the remaining half reducing by half in the next two minutes, and so on. (9, 58)

Force: A push or a pull which tends to change the motion of an object. (12, 28)

Frequency: The number of oscillations completed in one second. (70)

Gamma radiation: Electromagnetic waves which carry energy out of the nuclei of atoms. (7)

Gradient: An expression of the slope of a line on a graph. (33, 96)

Half-life (of a radioactive substance): The time taken for the amount of radioactive material present to have reduced to one half of its original value. (9)

Impulse: The product of the force applied to a body, multiplied by the time it is applied for. (42)

Insulator: A material that strongly resists the flow of electrons through it. (46)

Interference: The adding and cancelling out of two waves as they pass through the same area. (74, 76, 80)

Interference pattern: The alternating pattern of great disturbance and calm that is produced when two waves meet. (76)

Ion: A charged particle which is formed when electrons are removed from or added to an atom. (4)

Ionisation energy: The energy needed to pull electrons away from the positive nucleus of an atom. (4, 82)

Isotopes: Atoms of the same element with different masses. They have the same number of protons and electrons but different numbers of neutrons. (3)

Longitudinal wave: A wave in which the direction of oscillation is along the direction in which the wave is travelling. (72)

Mass: A measure of the amount of material in an object. (3, 15–19, 28, 36, 83)

Medium: The substance that a wave travels through. (72)

Momentum: A measure of the reluctance a moving object has to stopping – the product of its mass and velocity. (38–44)

Natural frequency: The frequency at which an object will vibrate freely. (71)

Neutron: A neutral particle found in the nuclei of atoms. It has a mass almost the same as that of a hydrogen atom. (3)

Normal (The): A straight line which is drawn at right angles to a surface, at a particular point. (74)

Nucleus: The central part of the atom which takes up very little space but contains most of the mass of the atom. (2)

Parallel circuit: An electric circuit where the current divides to flow through two or more components and then rejoins. (48, 51)

Potential difference: The difference in energy that one coulomb of charge has between two different points. (46, 49, 50)

Power: A measure of the rate of transforming energy. (25, 54)

Primary coil: The input coil of a transformer. (66)

Principle of superposition: The means by which we find the total displacement caused in a medium by more than one wave passing through – we add the separate displacements that each wave would produce. (77)

Proton: A positively charged particle found in the nuclei of atoms. It has a mass almost the same as that of a hydrogen atom. (2)

Reflection: When a wave rebounds from a surface which it hits, the rebounding path makes the same angle with the surface as did the incoming path. (74, 78)

Refraction: The change of direction of a wave as it moves from one medium into another. (74, 79)

Resultant vector: The vector formed by combining two or more vectors. (91)

Scalar: A measurement which requires only magnitude. (91)

Secondary coil: The output coil of a transformer. (66)

Series circuit: An electric circuit where the current must flow through each component in turn. (51)

Simple harmonic oscillators: Oscillators which always keep the same time period even though the amplitude may change. (21)

Speed: A measure of how fast an object is moving. Distance travelled divided by time taken. (29)

Standard form: A system of expressing numbers as a value between 1 and 10 multiplied by a power of ten. (88)

Time period: The time to complete one oscillation (sometimes called simply the period). (70)

Transformer: A device that transforms alternating potential difference and current. (57, 66)

Transverse wave: A wave in which the direction of oscillation is at right angles to the direction in which the wave is travelling. (72)

Vector: A measurement in which both magnitude and direction must be specified. (91)

Velocity: A measure of how fast an object is moving in a specified direction. (29)

Volt: The S.I. unit of electric current. (47)

Wavefront: Parts of the medium which are at the same point in their oscillation as a wave travels through it. (74)

Wavelength: The distance from any point on a wave to the corresponding point on the next wave. (72)

Weight: The force due to gravity acting on a mass. (16)

Work: The energy transformed by a moving force – the product of the force and the distance through which it moves in its own direction. (12–27)

Appendix

Units in physics

Base units

These units are defined by international agreement. All the other units are derived from these seven base units shown in Table A1.

Table A1   Base units

Quantity	Symbol of quantity	Unit	Symbol of unit
mass	m	kilogram	kg
length	l, d, s	metre	m
time	t	second	s
electric current	I	ampere (amp)	A
temperature	T	kelvin	K
luminous intensity	L	candela	cd
amount of substance	n, N	mole	mol

Derived units

These are derived from the base units shown in Table A1. They are derived using known physical relationships. For example we can use the relationship

$$\text{force} = \text{mass} \times \text{acceleration}$$

The base unit for mass is the kilogram and an acceleration is a velocity (measured in m/s) divided by a time (measured in seconds) and is therefore measured in m/s^2. So a force expressed in base units, would be measured in $kg\ m/s^2$. The derived unit of force is the newton, so 1 N is 1 $kg\ m/s^2$. All derived units can be expressed in terms of base units in this way.

Some of the more common derived units are shown in Table A2.

The symbols shown here are the ones commonly used, but they may differ in some books, so take care. Also note that you may find the same symbol used for different things, so you may have to consider the context in which the symbol is used.

SI units

The units indicated above are part of what is known as the Système International d'Unites or SI units. This means that the units all fit together in calculations giving a correct answer also in terms of an SI unit. If you used grams instead of kilograms in a calculation you would not get the correct answer.

Table A2   Commonly used derived units

Quantity	Symbol of quantity	Unit	Symbol of unit
acceleration	a		m/s^2
area	A, csa	square metre	m^2
atomic mass	A, amu	atomic mass unit	u
density	ρ		kg/m^3
electric capacitance	C	farad	F
electric charge	Q	coulomb	C
electric current	I	amp	A
electrical potential difference	V, pd	volt	V
electric resistance	R	ohm	Ω
energy, work, heat	W	joule	J
force	F	newton	N
frequency	f	hertz	Hz
gravitational field strength	g		N/kg
moment	m	newton metre	N m
momentum	p		kg m/s
power	P	watts	W
pressure	p	pascal	Pa, N/m^2
specific heat capacity	c		J/kg/K
specific latent heat	l		J/kg
torque	T	newton metre	N m
velocity	v, u		m/s

Prefixes

To make it easier to talk about large numbers and fractions, we can use standard prefixes for multiples of ten – see Table A3.

$$1/1000 \text{ watts} = 10^{-3} \text{ W} = 1 \text{ milliwatt} = 1 \text{ mW}$$

Table A3   Prefixes

Submultiple	Prefix	Symbol
10^{-3}	milli-	m
10^{-6}	micro-	μ
10^{-9}	nano-	n
10^{-12}	pico-	p

Multiple	Prefix	Symbol
10^3	kilo-	k
10^6	mega-	M
10^9	giga-	G
10^{12}	tera-	T

$$1\ 000\ 000 \text{ volts} = 10^6 \text{ V} = 1 \text{ megavolt} = 1 \text{ MV}$$

Formula list

Table A4 is a list of some of the most important formulae you will need for advanced physics.

Table A4   Useful formulae

Motion	Energy, work and power
speed $v = s/t$	$W = Fd$
acceleration $a = \dfrac{v - u}{t}$	$P = \dfrac{W}{t}$
$v = u + at$	$KE = \frac{1}{2}mv^2$
$v^2 = u^2 + 2as$	$GPE = mgh$
$s = ut + \frac{1}{2}at^2$	specific heat $= mcT$
	latent heat $= ml$
Mechanics and forces	efficiency $= \dfrac{\text{useful energy out}}{\text{energy in}} \times 100\%$
weight $F = mg$	
pressure $p = \dfrac{F}{A}$	$= \dfrac{\text{useful power out}}{\text{power in}} \times 100\%$
density $d = \dfrac{m}{V}$	**Electricity**
Hooke's law $F = kx$	$Q = It$
Newton's 2nd law $F = ma$	$V = IR$
momentum $p = mv$	$V = \dfrac{W}{Q}$
impulse $\Delta mv = Ft$	
moment $= Fd$	$P = VI = I^2R$
law of moments $F_1 \times d_1 = F_2 \times d_2$	$W = Pt = VIt$
Waves	series $R_t = R_1 + R_2 +$ etc.
$v = f\lambda$	parallel $\dfrac{1}{R_t} = \dfrac{1}{R_1} + \dfrac{1}{R_2} +$ etc.
$f = \dfrac{1}{T}$	Transformers $\dfrac{N_p}{N_s} = \dfrac{V_p}{V_s} = \dfrac{I_s}{I_p}$

Answers

Chapter 1

1 a 13, 33, 4, 55
  b 14, 42, 5, 78
  c 13, 33, 4, 55

2 $^{16}_8X$ and $^{17}_8X$; $^{14}_6X$ and $^{12}_6X$

3 The number of protons in the nucleus – more protons will hold the electron more tightly. The distance of the electrons from the nucleus – the closer they are, the more tightly they will be held.

4 1.2×10^6 m/s

  Note that this is only twice the velocity of a 1 eV electron.

5 An alpha particle spends more time in one area so it can affect more of the atoms. Therefore lots of ions form causing a thick track of droplets.

6 Thinner tracks mean fewer ions per mm.

7 As the alpha loses energy it slows down.

8 Atomic mass = 4, atomic number = 2.

9

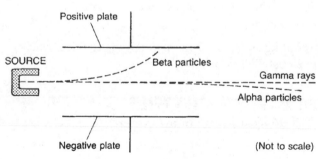

SOURCE

Positive plate

Beta particles

Gamma rays

Alpha particles

Negative plate   (Not to scale)

10 $1 = \alpha$, $2 = \beta$, $3 = \gamma$

11 a α; b γ; c β; d γ; e α; f α; g β; h γ;

12 $^{222}_{86}Rn \rightarrow ^{218}_{84}Po + ^{4}_{2}He$

13 a $^{211}_{82}Pb \rightarrow ^{211}_{83}Bi + ^{0}_{-1}e$
   b $^{221}_{87}Fr \rightarrow ^{217}_{85}At + ^{4}_{2}He$
   c $^{241}_{94}Pu \rightarrow ^{241}_{95}Am + ^{0}_{-1}e$
   d $^{231}_{90}Th \rightarrow ^{231}_{91}Pa + ^{0}_{-1}e$

14 a

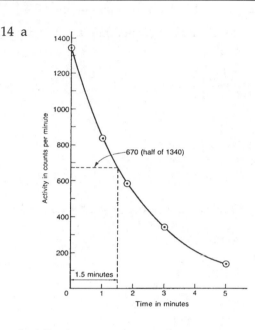

b 1.5 minutes – see graph
c $1340/8 = 167.5$ counts/second

15 344 counts/second

16 a $16 \times 5 = 80$ counts per minute
   b This is $\frac{1}{4}$ of the rate for the living wood, so it must be two half lives old i.e. $2 \times 5600 = 11\ 200$ years.

Chapter 2

1 c and d

2 1 264 000 J

3 400 N

4 120 m

5 a kinetic; b heat; c chemical; d electrical; e nuclear; f gravitational potential

6 3960 J

7 400 m

8 100 000 kg

9 250 m (i.e. 6.25 times higher)

10 a 6000 J; b 6000 J; c 60 kg

11 4000 J

12 1.8×10^7 J

13 93.8 J

14 8 m/s

15 250 kg

16 7.7 m/s

17 18 m

18 0.8 J

19 a 4 N each spring; b 10 cm; c total energy = 0.4 J

20 a Spring energy; b It is converted into kinetic energy; c 0.045 J; d 45 g

21 36 000 J

22 2100 J/kg/°C

23 60 000 J

24 a energy received per second
   = area of back × intensity
   = 0.5 m × 0.6 m × 800 J/s/m^2
   = 240 J
   b energy per hour = energy per second × 60 × 60
   = 864 000 J
   c mcT = 864 000 J
   70 × 4200 × T = 864 000
   294 000 × T = 864 000
   T = 864 000/294 000 = 2.94 °C
   d ml = 864 000 J
   m = 864 000/2 300 000
   = 0.376 kg (approx. 400 g)

25 100 800 J

26 1 A

27 233.3 V

28 222.2 s

29 129 s longer (871 s as against 1000 s)

30 117 W

31 5.18 × 10^6 J

32 15 500 s or 4.3 hours

33 13.5 minutes

34 10 800 J

35 31%

36 141 W

37 400 J

38 72 000 J

Chapter 3

1 Vector: force

2 a 0; b 300 N to the right; c 50 000 N upwards

3 a 0.5 km per minute due South;
   b 10 metres per second; c 1000 miles per hour

4 a 0.5 km per minute
   b stage 1:   0.8 km per minute approximately NE
   stage 2:   0.5 km per minute approximately N
   stage 3:   0.6 km per minute approximately W
   stage 4:   0.3 km per minute approximately S
   c stage 4

5 a 5 m/s along the track; b 325 m/s; c 25 m/s, 750 m

6 a i 1 (m/s)/s; ii 1.25 (m/s)/s; iii 1.67 (m/s)/s; iv 3.13 (m/s)/s; v 8.33 (m/s)/s;
   b 3 (m/s)/s
   c The cyclist will not be able to keep pedalling at that rate of power output.
   d 93 m/s

7 a 30 m/s; b 15 m/s; c 45 m

8 30 m/s; 300 m

9 600 m

10 180 N

11 200 000 N

12 2 (m/s)/s (in the direction opposite to its direction of travel); 15 s

13 220 000 N

14 1.8 × 10^{-14} N

15 1.8 s

16 500 N

17 70 m/s. No. Air resistance would reduce his acceleration.

18 a 700 kg m/s; b 12 m/s; c 80 kg; d 8 kg m/s; e 20 000 000 kg m/s

19 a 2.5 m/s
   b i 20 kg m/s; ii 4 kg m/s;
   iii 16 kg m/s; iv 16 m/s

20 5 m/s

21 6 × 10^{-12} m/s

22 a 5 m/s; b 0.125 m/s (Note: the individual also carries the gun.)

23 The momentum of the gun, bullet and firer is zero before firing. As the bullet is fired forward, the firer must move backwards with an equal and opposite amount of momentum to that of the bullet. The bullet's momentum will eventually be transferred to the victim who will therefore be thrown back as hard as the firer is thrown back.

24 $F × t$ = change in momentum
   $F × 0.09\,$s $= 1200$ kg $× 20$ m/s.
   $$F = \frac{24\,000}{0.09}N$$
   $$= 2.7 × 10^5 \text{ N}$$

25 a Gravity.
   b Friction between tyres and road surface.
   c Friction with the seat surface. This will be too small
     so the passenger tends to move in a straight line
     and slides along the seat. When he/she reaches the
     side of the passenger compartment the reaction
     force provides the centripetal force.

Chapter 4

1 60 C

2 2 A

3 a 1 A; b 10 A; c 15 A; d 5 A; e 3 A

4 a 10 J; b 24 J; c 1.6×10^{-18} J

5 7.3×10^7 m/s ($\frac{1}{4}$ of the speed of light!)

6 a 4 V; b 6 V; c 4.5 V

7 Thin wire.

8 a 66 Ω; b 0.92 Ω c 3.67 Ω

9 Voltmeter, across A, that is, in a parallel circuit across
   A. Ammeter, next to B, between B and the circuit
   junction.

10 All the ratios of V/I are the same, with a value of 10.
    b 10 Ω

11 2 Ω

12 4 A

13 a 10 Ω; b 1.5 A

14 a 2.18 Ω; b 5.5 A

15 45 Ω

16 2400 J

17 12 W

18 5 A; 7 A

19 360 000 J

20 Charging and discharging a capacitor is analogous to
    filling and emptying a water storage tank.

21 a

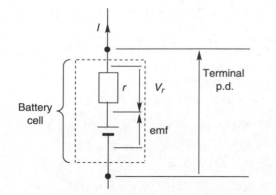

b emf = 15.5 V; internal resistance = 0.15 Ω
c 11 V

Chapter 5

1 A material that shows magnetic effects is iron. A
   magnet has two poles, termed the 'North pole' and
   'South pole'. Unlike poles attract, like poles repel.

2 The field looks exactly the same as that of the
   electromagnet in Fig 5.5.

3

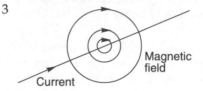

4 Yes it has.

5 The right-hand pole.

6 As just one of many examples: electromagnets can be
   used to pick out steel cans from aluminium cans in a
   recycling plant. The electromagnet can be switched off
   to allow the steel cans to drop into a receptacle.
   Electromagnets can be carefully controlled in strength,
   so are of use in, for example, medical applications
   such as the delicate process of removing iron splinters
   from the eye.

7 The strongest field is where the field lines are close
   together – at the bottom of the diagram. The field is
   weakest at the top of the diagram. The wire moves
   from strong field to weak.

8 a up; b down; c up

9 i Increase the magnetic field. ii Increase the number
   of turns on the coil. iii Increase the current through
   the coil.

10 a It does not need to revolve continuously.
    b i use more turns for the coil; ii use a weaker
       spring;
     iii use a stronger magnetic field

11 a B to A; b B to A

12 kinetic, electrical, electrical, kinetic

13 1 : 30

14 a 10 turns; b 3.1 A

15 a 7.5 A; b 9.4 A

Chapter 6

1 a 0.25 seconds; b 4 cycles per second (or hertz)

2 a swing: i C; ii A and D; iii B
   spring: i Y; ii W and Z; iii X
   b swing: distance C–D; spring: distance Y–Z

3 The swing should be pushed at its position of maximum displacement, in a direction towards the centre of the oscillation, once every full oscillation.

4 a transverse; b longitudinal; c transverse

5 Y is in exactly the same position as X, but on the next wave.

6 a 20 cm per second
   b 7.5 cm
   c 300 million metres per second
   d 1 090 909 hertz

7 a The frequency will not be affected since the same number of waves are still being produced every second.
   b The frequency, f, is unaltered but the wavelength is reduced. This means that the velocity, v, from $v = f\lambda$ must also reduce. This fits with the relationship.

8 a

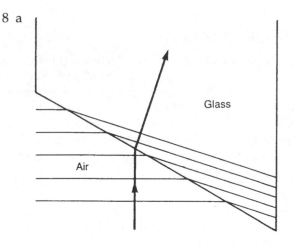

Glass

Air

   b It travels more slowly in glass.

9 a Inside the rectangle in photograph (a) and on the right in photograph (b).
   b In photograph (a) the whole wavefront moves on to the shallow region at the same time but in photograph (b) the right side of the wavefront is in the shallow region for a longer time than is the left. This means it falls behind.

10 a A few metres
   b a few hundredths of a millimetre

11

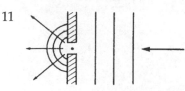

12 a 0.9 cm; b a high crest; c 4; d 3

13 a Trough from S_1
   b At B, two troughs will combine to produce a deep trough.
     At C, a crest combines with a trough to produce calm water.

14 Frequencies range from three hundred million million million (3×10^{20}) hertz in the gamma region, to three thousand hertz in the radio region.

15 They travel at the speed of light; they can be reflected, refracted, diffracted and show interference effects.

16 a Gamma rays, X-rays, ultra-violet, visible light, infra-red, microwaves, radio waves.
   b ultra-violet; 30 thousand million million hertz
   c one thousand million (10^9) times; X-rays

Chapter 7

1 This is twice 6.4×10^{-14} m so the force will be reduced to a quarter. Force $= 2.25$ N

2 a 6.4×10^{-13} J; b 1.6×10^{-12} J

3 $1 \text{ eV} = 1.6 \times 10^{-19}$ J

$1 \text{ MeV} = 1 \text{ eV} \times 10^6 = 1.6 \times 10^{-13}$ J
$$4.485 \times 10^{-12} \text{ J} = \frac{4.485 \times 10^{-12}}{1.6 \times 10^{-13}} \text{ MeV} = 28 \text{ MeV}$$

4 Binding energy per nucleon $= 28$ MeV$/4 = 7$ MeV

5 The binding energy is essentially energy which has been lost and so is a deficit. The negative sign signifies this.

6 1 kg U-235 $= 1000/235$ moles

$$= 4.255 \text{ moles}$$

1 mole $= 6.02 \times 10^{23}$ particles
so 4.255 moles $= 4.225 \times 6.02 \times 10^{23}$ particles
$$= 2.56 \times 10^{24} \text{ nuclei}$$

7 a 500 g $= 1.27 \times 10^{24}$ nuclei
   b energy yield $= 200 \times 2.54 \times 10^{24} = 5.08 \times 10^{26}$ MeV
   c energy in joules $= 2.56 \times 10^{26} \times 1.6 \times 10^{-19}$
$$= 4.096 \times 10^{13} \text{ J}$$

Chapter 8

1 a 1450; b 9 840 000; c 41.9;
   d 2.00; e 0.899; f 0.002 01

2 a 200; b 81; c 4.9; d 0.021; e 0.0060; f 100

3 a 300 000; b 2200; c 63 000 000; d 400;
   e 1 430 000; f 8189

4 a 1 000 000 or 10^6; b 10;
   c 830 000 000 000 or 8.3×10^{11};
   d 100 000 000 000 000 or 10^{14}
   e 28 000 000 000 or 2.8×10^{10}

5 a 10 000 or 10^4 b 10; c 50.42; d 200; e 4

6 a 10 000 or 10^4; b 3 000 or 3×10^3
   c 30 000 000 000 or 3×10^{10}; d 15; e 250

7 a 39 800; b 57 730 000; c 0.001 002;

d 8 224 000 000 000;

e 0.000 000 000 068 8; f 3.882

8 a 3.16×10^6; b 2.01×10^{-4}; c 1.03×10^0
d 5.33×10^{-8}; e 8.85×10^{10}

9 a $V = P/I$; $I = P/V$;
b $V = E/It$; $I = E/Vt$; $t = E/VI$;
c $t = (v - u)/a$;
$v = u + at$; $u = v - at$;
d $a = 2s/t^2$; $t = \sqrt{2s/a}$; e $m = 2E/v^2$;
$v = \sqrt{(2E/m)}$

10 a $v = (2d/t) - u$; b $h = v^2/2g$;
c i $v = 2E/p$;
ii $m = p^2/2E$;
d $u = v - (Ft/m)$; e $r = F/m\omega^2$

11 400 N 31°E of N

12 a 0.5; b 0.268; c 0.375

13 a 15.6 cm; b 11.9 cm; c 10.2 cm

14 a 36.9°; b 60°; c 41.8°

15 $F_1 = 14.1$ N; $F_2 = 10$ N

16 30°, tension = 2.07 N
45°, tension = 2.66 N
60°, tension = 2.31 N

17 forward force = 1360 N
force at right angles = 634 N

18 a $y = 2x + 1$; b P is related to Q (P^2 is proportional to Q);
c No relationship

19 a 0.16; b 0.35

20 a 4.6; b 9.2; c 14

The periodic table

Key

Relative atomic mass
Symbol
Name
Atomic number

Group

s-block · d-block · p-block · f-block

Period	I	II													III	IV	V	VI	VII	0
1	1.0 H Hydrogen 1																			4.0 He Helium 2
2	6.9 Li Lithium 3	9.0 Be Beryllium 4													10.8 B Boron 5	12.0 C Carbon 6	14.0 N Nitrogen 7	16.0 O Oxygen 8	19.0 F Fluorine 9	20.2 Ne Neon 10
3	23.0 Na Sodium 11	24.3 Mg Magnesium 12													27.0 Al Aluminium 13	28.1 Si Silicon 14	31.0 P Phosphorus 15	32.1 S Sulphur 16	35.5 Cl Chlorine 17	39.9 Ar Argon 18
4	39.1 K Potassium 19	40.1 Ca Calcium 20	45.0 Sc Scandium 21	47.9 Ti Titanium 22	50.9 V Vanadium 23	52.0 Cr Chromium 24	54.9 Mn Manganese 25	55.9 Fe Iron 26	58.9 Co Cobalt 27	58.7 Ni Nickel 28	63.5 Cu Copper 29	65.4 Zn Zinc 30	69.7 Ga Gallium 31	72.6 Ge Germanium 32	74.9 As Arsenic 33	79.0 Se Selenium 34	79.9 Br Bromine 35	83.8 Kr Krypton 36
5	85.5 Rb Rubidium 37	87.6 Sr Strontium 38	88.9 Y Yttrium 39	91.2 Zr Zirconium 40	92.9 Nb Niobium 41	95.9 Mo Molybdenum 42	(99) Tc Technetium 43	101.1 Ru Ruthenium 44	102.9 Rh Rhodium 45	106.4 Pd Palladium 46	107.9 Ag Silver 47	112.4 Cd Cadmium 48	114.8 In Indium 49	118.7 Sn Tin 50	121.8 Sb Antimony 51	127.6 Te Tellurium 52	126.9 I Iodine 53	131.3 Xe Xenon 54
6	132.9 Cs Caesium 55	137.3 Ba Barium 56	138.9 La Lanthanum 57 *	178.5 Hf Hafnium 72	181.0 Ta Tantalum 73	183.9 W Tungsten 74	186.2 Re Rhenium 75	190.2 Os Osmium 76	192.2 Ir Iridium 77	195.1 Pt Platinum 78	197.0 Au Gold 79	200.6 Hg Mercury 80	204.4 Tl Thallium 81	207.2 Pb Lead 82	209.0 Bi Bismuth 83	(210) Po Polonium 84	(210) At Astatine 85	(222) Rn Radon 86
7	(223) Fr Francium 87	(226) Ra Radium 88	(227) Ac Actinium 89 †	(261) Db Dubnium 104	(262) Jl Joliotium 105	(263) Rf Rutherfordium 106	(262) Bh Bohrium 107	(?) Hn Hahnium 108	(?) Mt Meitnerium 109									

*Lanthanides

140.1 Ce Cerium 58	140.9 Pr Praseodymium 59	144.2 Nd Neodymium 60	(147) Pm Promethium 61	150.4 Sm Samarium 62	152.0 Eu Europium 63	157.3 Gd Gadolinium 64	158.9 Tb Terbium 65	162.5 Dy Dysprosium 66	164.9 Ho Holmium 67	167.3 Er Erbium 68	168.9 Tm Thulium 69	173.0 Yb Ytterbium 70	175.0 Lu Lutetium 71

†Actinides

232.0 Th Thorium 90	(231) Pa Protactinium 91	238.1 U Uranium 92	(237) Np Neptunium 93	(242) Pu Plutonium 94	(243) Am Americium 95	(247) Cm Curium 96	(245) Bk Berkelium 97	(251) Cf Californium 98	(254) Es Einsteinium 99	(253) Fm Fermium 100	(256) Md Mendelevium 101	(254) No Nobelium 102	(257) Lr Lawrencium 103